ADVANCE PRAISE

"Space superiority is one of the most important goals for long-term American survival. Greg Autry and Peter Navarro clearly describe the challenges we face in outer space—and the devastating consequences if America cedes space leadership to other nations. The dangers we face are real. If we don't confront them, the future could be catastrophic for America and the world."

—**Newt Gingrich**, 50th Speaker of the United States House of Representatives

"This superbly researched book is equivalent to the warnings by Winston Churchill in the 1930s regarding the catastrophic failure of leadership by the West to counter Nazi Germany and the Empire of Japan before the onset of WWII. In this case, it documents the very real threat to the American way of life posed by communist China's rapidly growing space-based offensive capabilities. A convincing case is made that we will prevail only when our leaders acknowledge the obvious: we are in a second space race with an adversary whose ambitions to expand its autocratic rule knows no geographic bounds, extending to near-Earth and cis-lunar space. If we prevail in this space race—which makes the one with the Soviets in the 1960s look like child's play by comparison—the political, social, and economic benefits to the world will be beyond measure."

—**Courtney Stadd**, Former Director, Commercial Space Policy at the White House National Space Council; Former NASA Chief of Staff; and currently Executive Vice President, Beyond Earth Institute

"This book needs to be on the desk of every official in the Pentagon, Congress, the White House, and the Western World, not to mention everyone who wants to understand the Space Race 2.0 now fully engaged between the USA and China in the context of a world that is increasingly hostile to the values of our American republic and Western civilization in general."

—**Homer Hickam**, NASA Engineer and
Author of *Rocket Boys* (aka *October Sky*)

"*The* threat of the 21st century...the authors nailed it. The United States *is* an aerospace nation...from the beaches of Kitty Hawk to the International Space Station to the James Webb Space Telescope and beyond...this and all of the benefits of access to and use of space for the betterment of humankind are at risk. Our adversaries view competition as conflict and we are in conflict today. Imagine a 'day without space'...it is closer than you think. The authors paint a clear picture of the threats to the free use of space from basic commerce to international security. A must-read!"

—**Major General Lee Levy (Ret.)**, Member
of the NASA Advisory Council

"Autry and Navarro provide a compelling overview of the status and stakes of the new space race, the reasons America must win, and a plan to do it. Highly entertaining and super-informative even for the expert, this is a must-read for every voter, taxpayer, and parent who is concerned about America's future and whether our best days will be behind us or yet ahead."

—**Peter Garretson, Lt. Col., USAF (Ret.)**, Author
of *Scramble for the Skies* and *The Next Space Race*

"Autry and Navarro have been way ahead of the curve in warning of the dire consequences of China's expanding technological capabilities. Time to wake up and get serious. Read the book."

—**Honorable Dana Rohrabacher**, Long-Serving
Chair of the House Space Subcommittee

"*Red Moon Rising* highlights important threats that we would face during a future conflict with China in space, from electromagnetic pulse nuclear explosions to kinetic as well as non-kinetic anti-satellite attacks. One thing is certain—China does not intend to lose the Space Race 2.0. I can personally attest to China's military capabilities in space. While I was Commander of the International Space Station in 2015, we were forced to maneuver to avoid debris still in orbit from China's ill-advised anti-satellite weapon demonstration in 2007. Then, a few months later, while looking out the window one night at the darkness of Western China, I suddenly saw a disorienting bright flash. I had been lased from a ground station in China. These two incidents left no doubt in my mind that our Chinese friends have plans to dominate the space domain. And if that were allowed to happen it would be very bad for all freedom-loving people down here on Earth."

—**Colonel Terry Virts (Ret.)**, Former NASA
Astronaut, Commander of the International
Space Station, USAF F-16 Pilot and Test Pilot

"Greg Autry's and Peter Navarro's book is a must-read for anyone looking to understand where the United States stands in space leadership. Their theme is the Chinese challenge to gain space supremacy, and they make it quite vivid. But it is the history of how we got to where we are that adds perspective. The description of the rise of commercial space as both a partner with and a competitor to government-led programs is a valuable glimpse of the future. Autry and Navarro capture history, competition, national security, and challenge in a most entertaining and illuminating read."

—**Congressman Robert S. Walker (Ret.)**, Former Chairman of the House Committee on Science, Space and Technology, CEO of MoonWalker Associates

"During the Trump administration, Autry and Navarro were influential in defining the most important and successful US space agenda since the 1960s. I had the opportunity to watch them at work and they were informed, determined, and fearless. Much remains to be done, and in this important book, they detail the challenges our nation faces in space as well as the immense opportunities the development of the Moon and solar system can bring to our people and all humankind."

—**Steve Kwast, Lt. General USAF (Ret.)**, CEO of SpaceBilt Inc.

"*Red Moon Rising: How America Will Beat China on the Final Frontier* is a study in common sense. Autry and Navarro adeptly make the case for space exploration with pragmatic alacrity while describing China's space ambitions in level-headed, matter-of-fact prose that builds an undeniable reality. Tracking the evolution of China's space objectives, they point out China's stated goal of becoming the world's dominant space power and explain how China can 'make it so.' As a space lawyer, I appreciate the perspective provided, as it offers crucial insights for navigating the complex legal challenges arising from China's rising influence in outer space activities. It is imperative that policymakers understand the implications not just for law, but for access to space and its resources. Written with urgency rather than alarm, this is must-read book is an excellent study in geopolitics that will undoubtedly spur discussion, and hopefully, action."

—**Michelle L.D. Hanlon**, Executive Director, Center for Air and Space Law at the University of Mississippi

"A military maxim is to dominate the high ground to defeat the enemy, and none is higher than space. Autry and Navarro's exceptional book explains why space matters to Americans and to US national security, and why Communist China's strategic bid for supremacy in space must be defeated by the US. One of the reasons this book is particularly valuable and relevant is that it shows Communist China's ambitions are not just global, but truly extend to lunar and planetary dominance. In this comprehensive study, the authors present Beijing's extensive and multifaceted capabilities and how it employs space today to harm US interests as well as the key role space will play in the event Communist China starts a war. This is a powerful, insightful, and witty analysis of why the US must command the high ground to ensure the security of Americans, our allies, and key partners."

—**Dr. Bradley A. Thayer**, Founding Member of the Committee on Present Danger China and Coauthor of *Embracing Communist China: America's Greatest Strategic Failure, Understanding the China Threat,* and *How China Sees the World: Han-Centrism and the Balance of Power in International Politics*

"Today millions of Americans, and billions more around the planet, are reliant upon space-based systems for their daily lives and existence. Whether accessing their finances, communicating with family and friends, their life's history in picture or video, or even access to healthcare, the world is now dependent upon access to space. Since Operation Desert Storm in 1991, battlefields around the globe are now dominated by precision guided weapons that are reliant on access to space-based intelligence satellites. Simply put, space is an essential domain that must be protected. Unfortunately one nation has demonstrated their intention to dominate the space domain through non-kinetic and kinetic means—the People's Republic of China (PRC). In *Red Moon Rising*, Autry and Navarro provide a comprehensive analysis of this critical domain, the threats posed by the PRC, and the solutions necessary to ensure America, and our allies, are able to keep this domain free and open for ourselves and our posterity. This is a must-read for those who wish to be informed and who wish to petition their representatives to take corrective actions now."

—**James E. Fanell, CAPT USN (Ret.)**, Former Director of Intelligence and Information Operations for the US Pacific Fleet, Founding Member of the Committee on Present Danger China, and Coauthor of *Embracing Communist China: America's Greatest Strategic Failure*

"We had better get American boots on the moon before the Chinese do. The Communists in Beijing tell us they will prevent us from going there if they arrive first, and whoever controls the moon will end up dominating just about everything else in the solar system, including our planet. Yes, the moon is that important, so now's a great time to find out what Greg Autry and Peter Navarro have to tell us in *Red Moon Rising*."

—**Gordon Chang**, Author of *The Great U.S.-China Tech War* and *China Is Going to War*

ALSO BY GREG AUTRY

A New Entrepreneurial Dynamic:
21st Century Startups and Small Businesses

ALSO BY PETER NAVARRO

Taking Back Trump's America: Why We Lost the
White House and How We'll Win It Back

The True Meaning of Trump's MAGA: Lessons from
the 2022 Republican Red Wave That Never Happened

ALSO BY GREG AUTRY AND PETER NAVARRO

Death by China: Confronting the Dragon –
A Global Call to Action

RED MOON RISING

How America Will Beat China
on the Final Frontier

GREG AUTRY & PETER NAVARRO

Foreword by DOUGLAS LOVERRO

Post Hill
PRESS

A POST HILL PRESS BOOK
ISBN: 979-8-88845-516-6
ISBN (eBook): 979-8-88845-517-3

Red Moon Rising:
How America Will Beat China on the Final Frontier
© 2024 by Greg Autry and Peter Navarro
All Rights Reserved

Cover photo by Greg Autry

This is a work of nonfiction. All people, locations, events, and situations are portrayed to the best of the author's memory.

Post Hill Press
New York • Nashville
posthillpress.com

Published in the United States of America
1 2 3 4 5 6 7 8 9 10

To Homer Hickam for making us care about the future, and to Stuart O. Witt for giving the future permission to arrive.

Do not pray for fair weather. Pray for courage.
—Papa Mau Piailug, Master Polynesian Navigator

TABLE OF CONTENTS

FOREWORD

All armies prefer high ground to low, and sunny
places to dark... With regard to precipitous heights, if
you are beforehand with your adversary, you should
occupy the raised and sunny spots, and there wait
for him to come up.
—Sun Tzu, *The Art of War*

I t is hard to imagine that Sun Tzu ever conceived of as precipitous a height or as sunny a spot as Earth orbit. But it is
abundantly clear that the leaders of China's Communist Party
(CCP) recognize the power of applying this centuries-old wisdom in the most modern of contexts—space. You are about to
read a book that exposes the frightening implications of that
totalitarian epiphany. It also tells the engrossing tale of how
we got here, with humor and with the lessons learned clearly
marked for the consideration of current and future policy
makers. *Red Moon Rising* also reveals the powerful benefits
that will accrue to everyone on Earth if America wins this
second space race.

At the close of the 20th century, China was, by all mea-
sures, a minor space power. Despite Mao's post-Sputnik pro-
nouncements that China would soon mirror the success of
their Soviet neighbors, the Chinese space program moved
slowly. Their objective, to launch a satellite into orbit on the
tenth anniversary of the founding of the PRC in 1959, came

and went—it would take another eleven years for China to reach space with its first satellite. China's human spaceflight program began in 1967 and was mothballed four years later. While the Chinese space efforts for the next fifteen years made some slow progress, they lacked a clear national focus.

Meanwhile, the US demonstrated the remarkable power of aerospace R&D to turbocharge a nation's scientific and economic engine. Between 1954 and the moon landing in 1969, the US undertook three massive, highly technological space and missile developments—the Minuteman and Polaris ICBM programs and NASA's multifaceted space program including Mercury, Gemini, and Apollo. These efforts pumped over seven trillion inflation-adjusted dollars into America's ready industrial base, a manufacturing monster built during World War II. By comparison, that huge war had cost the nation just five trillion current-day dollars. 2021's Infrastructure Act looks almost parsimonious by comparison at $1.2 trillion.

However, the multiplier effect of those space-related expenditures was much higher than with other investments. Addressing Columbia University's graduating class in 1955, CIA Director Allen Dulles noted that the Soviet Union was graduating 120,000 students in science and engineering while the US had just 70,000, less than 20 percent of American graduates. By 1970, interest in aerospace careers had pushed STEM students to 284,000, over 35 percent of degrees conferred. While space had inspired them, many of these graduates would find careers in aviation, electronics, and software. Space and missile development raised the intellectual capital America needed to dominate the tech sector for half a century.

China woke up to that. In 1986, four Chinese scientists wrote a letter to then paramount leader Deng Xiaoping proposing the "863 program," or State High-Tech Development Plan, which was intended to replicate the impact of US technological developments in China. Among other things, 863 secretly revived the Chinese human spaceflight program. This investment paid off. By the turn of the millennium, China had a human-capable spaceflight system, Shenzhou-1, and in 2003 they launched China's first "taikonaut" into orbit.

The impact of these public investments mirrored successes in the US. In 1988, China had fewer than two hundred thousand graduates in science and engineering—about a tenth of America per capita. By the time of their first manned space launch, Chinese STEM grads had doubled and were half the US. In 2020, China graduated 3.5 million students in STEM career fields, leaving America a very distant third, behind India.

Competitions between rival nations are determined by how resources are applied. China's leaders are highly focused on space, specifically in the service of military functions. Their military strategists have taken careful note of the shift in US warfighting doctrine, strategy, and capabilities brought on by enhanced space capabilities. The integration of US space assets into its non-nuclear warfighting machine began in the 1990s but was still minimal in the First Gulf War; GPS had yet to be fully fielded; most space imagery was still unavailable to tactical forces. US missile detection systems could barely pinpoint short burning Scud missiles, and if they did, the information could not be relayed to the field in time to strike the launchers before they scooted away. Added to the lack of robust satellite communications capabilities, these shortfalls in space integration forced the US and their coalition partners to deploy over 730,000 personnel, including half a million US servicemembers, to the Gulf.

In contrast, the American forces in Afghanistan and Iraq for Operations Enduring and Iraqi Freedom (OEF and OIF) never exceeded 180,000, despite the vastly larger and more challenging scope of those operations. Integration of space into everyday military operations had provided America with the ability to achieve far more on the ground with far fewer personnel at risk. The impact of this shift, from non-space to space-enabled forces on the battlefield, was noted by Chinese military planners. Some of them were already looking to counter this advantage. In 2000, Chinese strategist Wang Hucheng noted that space was becoming America's "soft ribs" and counseled his superiors that, "For countries that can never win a war with the United States by using the method of tanks and planes, attacking the U.S. space system may be an irresistible and most tempting choice."

On January 11, 2001, the Rumsfeld Space Commission issued a report warning of a "Space Pearl Harbor." Exactly six years to the day later, China launched a destructive anti-satellite test that demonstrated their ability to find America's soft ribs.

American military leaders struggled with how to react to this new threat for a decade and some were even ready to abandon space—which I and many others recognized was the wrong approach. While the integration of space into US warfighting was relatively new, it represented a trend in precision engagement and remote operations that had been building for decades. Not only did the US prefer to fight wars that way, it also concluded that the best way to deter Chinese ambitions was by continuing to integrate space into combat operations. If that advantage was at risk, our entire Indo-Pacific strategy was as well. Vice Chair of the Joint Chiefs of Staff General

John Hyten warned that war without space would boomerang the US back to "industrialized warfare"—the World War II model, where body counts and manufacturing capacity determine the victor—a clear win for China.

Today, the range of demonstrated Chinese operational and test space weaponry is impressive and growing, and you'll learn some frightening things about them in this book. This threat inspired a bipartisan group of US space strategists and leaders (including both myself and Dr. Autry) to push for the creation of a US Space Force, which was finally stood up under the Trump administration. Good but perhaps too late given the speed and boldness of China's aggressive space warfare posture.

The Chinese are not only threatening to disable US space capabilities—they are building their own space-enabled offensive infrastructure. In this way, they can not only rob the US of its keystone for power projection, but also threaten US ground, naval, and air forces outside the Chinese second island chain in places like Guam, Kwajalein, the Philippines, and the open Pacific. This threat cannot be overstated: for the first time since World War II, US forces may have to contend with a peer adversary who can find, fix, track, and target US terrestrial forces from afar—a condition under which US forces have not operated for over three-quarters of a century. Chinese space power changes the calculus of US warfighting in ways we are only now just recognizing.

And it gets worse. The story of why space matters in the contest between the US and China extends beyond warfare. As you'll discover in *Red Moon Rising*, it's an economic story, a resources story, a technology leadership story, an energy independence story, and perhaps most importantly, an international prestige story. When President Kennedy proposed the Apollo Program to the US Congress, scarcely six weeks after Yuri Gagarin's historic flight, he noted that "...the dramatic achievements in space which occurred in recent weeks should have made clear to us all, as did the Sputnik in 1957, the impact of this adventure on the minds of men everywhere who are attempting to make a determination of which road they should take..." Thankfully, the Apollo Moon walkers demonstrated to the world that the road marked "democracy" and "capitalism" was the proper course.

Those Apollo pioneers are sadly passing, and the lessons learned are unfortunately dimming. Today the nations of the world are again looking at two paths to the future. Chinese space accomplishments threaten to detour the world away from Western ideals and toward an ideology that is antithetical to all we value. Whether by use in war, or as a proxy for world leadership, space will play a leading role in this contest. As the authors of this book will illustrate to you, America dares not falter.

—**Doug Loverro**
Washington DC
January 12, 2024

Colonel (retired) Doug Loverro, a 1976 graduate of the Air Force Academy, served thirty years in the Air Force, leading space programs like GPS, AF Space Control, and National Reconnaissance Office (NRO) Radar and Optical Imagery Programs. Following his retirement in 2006, he served for eleven more years as Deputy for System Engineering at the NRO, Executive Director of all AF Space Programs at the Space and

Missile Systems Center, and finally as Deputy Assistant Secretary of Defense for Space Policy in the Pentagon for President Obama. He retired from government in 2017 but was called back briefly in 2019 to lead all Human Space Exploration for NASA under President Trump. For the last six years, he has been an independent consultant with clients across the space industry, the Pentagon, Congress, and the White House. He is widely recognized as one of the nation's most strategically focused space leaders.

THE MOON IS KEEPING US UP AT NIGHT

*I do not believe that this generation of Americans is
willing to resign itself to going to bed each night by
the light of a Communist moon.*
—Lyndon Baines Johnson,
Senate Floor, October 1957

"**W**hy should the American government or billionaires be spending money in space when we have problems right here on Earth?" This is a question that advocates for NASA space exploration, space development, and space tourism are frequently forced to answer. It's a fair question, and all too often, the answers of scientists and engineers have not satisfied.

As you will learn from this book, public and private space investments have delivered numerous benefits to those of us on Earth. Spoiler alert: these include GPS, weather forecasts, global communications, medical technologies, and much more. Research going on in space today promises revolutionary developments in pharmaceuticals, semiconductors, and miraculous materials. If you care about the environment, you'll discover the best environmental data and solutions (solar, fuel cells…) were developed for space.

More immediately important, a second Cold War is now upon us, this time with Communist China. It comes at a time when we face a cornucopia of domestic problems. Many, if not most of the economic, political, and social ills that plague our nation and world, are manifestations of a failure to confront the malfeasance of China's Communist Party. You are living in the dystopian future that we warned of more than a decade ago in a previous book, *Death by China: Confronting the Dragon—A Global Call to Action* (2011, Pearson). The task of confronting the Dragon is now existential. The fight can no longer be left to future generations. Like the previous one, Cold War 2.0 comes with a space race, this time with China. We will keep our eye on Space Race 2.0 throughout this text.

As you might recall, America won the first space race on July 20, 1969, when Neil Armstrong and Buzz Aldrin kicked up dust on the Moon. Their two-hour stroll on the surface of another world demonstrated that the Soviet Union was no match for America's superior technology and economic power. By extension, it sent a clear message to the world that our political, civil, and educational systems, based on democracy, the rule of law, and individual freedom, delivered the goods far better than Moscow's dreary socialist model. Tom Wolfe framed this most clearly in his novel *The Right Stuff*, where he wrote of America's astronauts, "The men chosen for this historic mission took on the archaic mantles of the single-combat warriors of a long-since-forgotten time…They were risking their lives for their country, for their people."

Almost immediately after their failure to reach the Moon, the Soviet Union began its long downward spiral. Detente and eventually perestroika followed. Reagan's Strategic Defense Initiative (aka "Star Wars") leveraged the perception of American space superiority to drive a stake through the heart of that Evil Empire. Before any nuclear space shield could be deployed, Mikhail Gorbachev had the good sense to fold his cards and surrender Cold War 1.0. Nuclear Armageddon was postponed, and the peace dividend was paid out. Two generations of Americans have grown up without the formative experience of huddling in fear under their desk during nuclear attack drills.

With China's rise, new horrors from space may await us all. The disturbing scenarios in this book are designed to keep you up at night with us. You will also learn how the competition from China is accelerating America's efforts in space in ways that can provide our nation and all the people of the world a brighter future. We hope you will be alarmed, inspired, and motivated.

CHAPTER TEN

LIKE A BOLT OUT OF THE BLACK: FIRST, LET US SCARE YOU

The blue-black tropical night suddenly turned into a hot lime green. It was brighter than noon. The green changed into a lemonade pink and finally, terribly, blood red. It was as if someone had poured a bucket of blood on the sky.
—Thomas Thompson, *LIFE*[1]

U nless you happen to be outside at night, you won't have a clue that anything dramatic has occurred hundreds of miles above your home. You will notice the instantaneous deactivation of everything in your digital world. The failure of the tablet that you're reading this book on or the noise-canceling headphones you're using to listen to this audiobook might be your first clue. You'll soon realize your lights are out, the AC is off, and your precious mobile phone is a brick. No cable TV, no old-school radio, no landline, you'll have absolutely no way to figure out what just happened. Being unable to get onto

X (formerly Twitter) or Facebook to check with your friends and family is going to turn out to be the least of your problems…. Chinese space weaponry has just transported your butt into the Stone Age.

WE KNOW IT WORKS…BECAUSE WE TRIED IT

On the night of Sunday, July 8, 1962, the residents of Honolulu stayed up late. They gathered on the beaches of the North Shore, on hotel roofs in Waikiki, and on Oahu's dramatic mountain ridges. Kailua resident Alan Lloyd was on a hill above Salt Lake, not far from the international airport. It was a warm tropical evening filled with clouds drifting in the trade winds. Suddenly, there was a brilliant flash, and as Lloyd recalled, "The whole world lit up right away and then the whole sky turned red and stayed that way for about 20 minutes."[2] Photos taken that night show Waikiki Beach and Diamond Head illuminated as though it were midday. The awe-inspiring flare was reported by observers on ships and islands more than 1,000 miles away.[3] After their eyes readjusted, viewers beheld a tropical aurora spreading far across the South Pacific sky.

The people of Hawaii had stayed up to watch the "rainbow bomb," a 1.4 megaton thermonuclear warhead known to the US military as Starfish Prime. Built at the Los Alamos Laboratory, it had been lofted into space aboard a Thor rocket, from Johnston Atoll, nine hundred miles west-southwest of Hawaii. The nuke was detonated 250 miles up, at the same altitude where the International Space Station (ISS) now peacefully circles Earth.

Starfish Prime was part of a broader operation run by the US Atomic Energy Commission and the Defense Atomic

Support Agency, known as Operation Fishbowl. Fishbowl was America's response to a resumption of active nuclear testing by the Soviet Union, which had broken a three-year mutual testing moratorium. In the next few months, as the Cuban Missile Crisis heated up, the two countries would blow up several more A-bombs in space.[4] The stakes were a lot higher than the aerial light shows suggested.

More important than the dramatic space fireworks were reports that radio stations in Honolulu were suddenly silenced by the blast and that the streets of Manoa Valley and Kailua went dark as Hawaiian Electric's grid suffered multiple failures. Hundreds of streetlights on thirty circuits remained down for some time because their transformers had suffered permanent damage. These disturbances were generated by a phenomenon known as an electromagnetic pulse, or EMP, a result of the massive ionization that occurs in a nuclear explosion as electrons are ripped from the nuclei of atoms in the blast zone. Starfish Prime's EMP exceeded the expectations of the US brass and in some cases, pegged the dials on the measurement devices American scientists were using to monitor the effects of the blast.[5] The electrical hardware of the time was crude by today's standards. If Starfish Prime blew today, the sensitive semiconductors inside just about everything we depend on could be permanently toasted.

If some hostile country, say China, detonated an EMP space bomb over a city like Taipei, Tokyo, or Tampa, the results would be catastrophic. Life as you know it would come to a halt, perhaps very literally. Anyone with a pacemaker would drop dead in front of your eyes. Hospital life-support equipment, including their emergency backup power systems, will be as fried as your phone. Automobile and aircraft electronics, including autonomous driving computers, will instantly lose control. Electrical transformers will explode, and the electric car in your garage could turn into a raging fireball. Roads and highways will be permanently clogged with dead cars, the microprocessors regulating their modern internal combustion engines wrecked.

And none of your stuff is coming back online anytime soon, if ever. Repair crews are not on their way because they are as disabled as anyone. None of the emergency vehicles, tow trucks, or construction equipment required for the job are moving. There aren't enough replacement transformers, generators, microchips, or anything else on hand to fix this. Worse, the supply chain for those critical items runs through the port of Shanghai, where you can bet they are not busy loading relief ships for America. Without power or transportation, food and water will not last more than a week. Everyone will quickly realize they need to grab what is available for themselves. Things will turn ugly and fast. It's time for Gen Z to crawl out of their safe spaces and learn how to make a fire and sharpen a spear, all without the guidance of a mansplaining YouTube video from some crazy prepper.

COULD THEY, WOULD THEY, IF THEY COULD?

Why would China blow up a nuke in space instead of just roasting our cities with a good old-fashioned mushroom cloud? There are several reasons. The first of which is that a space detonation leaves the ground unscathed and free of lingering radiation. Most tourists enjoying their Hawaiian vacations are clueless to the fact that Honolulu witnessed five of these rainbow bombs in the early '60s. Using such a "clean" weapon is much less unthinkable than crossing the boundary to the horrors of Hiroshima.

If China chose to take Taiwan or to occupy and repopulate Korea, Japan, or Vietnam with Han Chinese settlers—as they are now doing in Tibet,[6] Mongolia,[7] and East Turkestan[8]—an EMP will render their opponents helpless, without the stigma of a "nuclear attack." Would the US intervene? Our current leadership would probably just burn some taxpayer funds in a hopeless gesture. China's "factory floor of the world" will easily replace those transformers and car parts and reboot their new territories. Letting their victims stew in hell for a few months after the attack will reduce and cow the native population, allowing China to avoid the muss and fuss of the concentration camps and executions utilized in their current ethnic cleansing campaigns.

We know that China has been hard at work on high-altitude electromagnetic pulse weapons, or HEMPs, designing smaller low-yield nukes specifically intended to generate stronger magnetic fields and maximize electronic destruction. US intelligence sources also believe China has tested chemical-based EMPs with hypersonic delivery systems and microwave systems that could be deployed from space.

Readily available Chinese military documents not only reveal the ability to deploy these weapons but make frighteningly clear that Beijing views HEMPs as a class of "cyberweapons" unconstrained by the international agreements and norms that have so long controlled the use of traditional nuclear arms.[9] China has been openly conducting cyberwarfare assaults on US governmental and commercial systems for years. With cyberattacks being seen as a gray area, our diplomatic and military leaders have stood by helpless and mostly mute as critical American systems are impinged on the daily. This farce has included watching Google's source code and the personnel records of nearly every federal employee being stolen by proxies of the Chinese state.[10] See our 2011 book, *Death by China: Confronting the Dragon*, for more details on this one-sided war in progress.[11]

Underscoring their "EMPs aren't really even an act of war" doctrine, China's state mouthpiece, *The Global Times*, reported that Chinese military experts were promoting the use of EMPs against US warships because "they can temporarily paralyze US ships' weapon and control systems without visible conflict...."[12]

Russia has taken a similar stand. A report by the executive director of the EMP Task Force on National and Homeland Security reads, "Russian military doctrine, because HEMPs destroy only electronics, categorizes nuclear HEMP attack as a dimension of Information Warfare, Electronic Warfare and Cyber Warfare" and "Russia has 'Super-EMP' weapons specialized for HEMP attack that potentially generate 100,000 volts/meter or higher, greatly exceeding the U.S. military hardening standard."

Indeed, in February of 2024, a congressional leak of information about a Russian nuclear space weapon created hysteria on the Hill and in the media. The device appeared to be an anti-satellite EMP.[13]

CHINA WATCHES AND LEARNS

The 1991 Gulf War has often been called, "The First Space War." In its stunningly speedy victory over Saddam Hussein's Iraqi forces, America's GPS-enabled ground forces stormed across the featureless Iraqi desert. The US Army's fully integrated battlefield, space-based communications network cleared the "fog of war" for the allied side, and imaging satellites provided speedy damage assessments to commanders.[14] China carefully watched all this and vowed to capture these space-based advantages—and much more—for themselves.

CHINA WILL NOT REPEAT ITS BIGGEST BLUNDER

Space Race 1.0, of the 1960s, was a glorious competition of technological demonstrations aimed at domestic and international audiences. Space Race 2.0 is about the economic development of space and its real strategic advantages. As was the case in the last age of exploration, the cultures and political systems that settle space and exploit its resources will define the future of human civilization for centuries. Nations that choose not to participate will vanish or be subjugated by the wealthier holders of the celestial high ground.

In the early fifteenth century, the Ming Dynasty was sending bold voyages of exploration around the globe. Large fleets of massive ships hauled treasures and exotic beasts back from India, Africa, and the Middle East. Reaching the Americas—decades before Columbus—was nearly within their reach.[i] Internal court intrigues and a comet deemed to be a bad omen resulted in the cancellation of the exploration program. China then chose to turn inward and focus on their "problems right here at home" while Europeans conquered the globe. Expansive Western powers and a rapidly mod-

---

i   See *When China Ruled the Seas: The Treasure Fleet of the Dragon Throne, 1405–1433* by Louise Levathes. For a very entertaining narrative intertwined with a great deal of questionable analysis, see Gavin Menzies's highly speculative *1421: The Year China Discovered America.*

ernizing Japanese Empire ran roughshod over the Middle
Kingdom. The "century of humiliation" under the bootheels
of foreign economic and military forces is burned into the
Chinese psyche. That painful history weighs heavily on their
approach to space exploration and development. They do not
intend to lose Space Race 2.0.

China is determined not to be eclipsed in the coming
age of space exploration. Xi Jinping has clearly stated that
the "China Space Dream" is to be the world's dominant space
power.[15] China Aerospace Science and Technology Corporation (CASC) has publicly set the date of China's space ascen-
dancy to 2045.[16]

BUT WAIT, THERE'S MORE!

So, before we get to the happier part of this book, let's consider what else might be lurking in China's bag of space horrors.
An EMP attack is one good way for China to disable enemy
satellites across a wide area of space. An EMP could disable or
permanently fry the electronics across hundreds of miles and
last long enough for dozens of satellites to pass through its
hazardous cloud of plasma. This wide dispersion and lasting
effects pose the dilemma of taking out China's own surveillance and communications systems that overfly the territory
they are trying to attack. Being blind and deaf in the theater
of operations is not on the top of any general's environmental choices. It also risks damaging space assets that belong to
China's client states, such as Iran or China's nominal space
ally, Russia. There is no value in ticking off a bunch of unpre-
dictable folks who don't really trust Beijing anyway.

ANTI-SATELLITE SYSTEMS (ASATS), A SMASHING IDEA

So, while they will keep the EMP in their pocket, precision anti-satellite weapons (ASATs) are likely to be favored by China for something like the invasion of Taiwan. The most common ASAT variant is the kinetic kill vehicle, a missile that simply smacks into an opponent's satellite, quickly reducing it to debris. This method is much less immediately dangerous to yourself and your partners in crime. It does, however, potentially create a hazardous cloud of debris in orbit, which puts every spacefaring nation at risk for eventual collisions.

In fact, China did just this in January 2007 when they used an SC-19 ASAT missile to destroy one of their own FY-1C satellites in a polar orbit. Firing the missile from the ground to an orbital interception is known as a "direct ascent test." This test created the largest and most dangerous debris field in space, with over three thousand pieces tracked from the ground and tens of thousands of smaller ones unaccounted for.[17] About a third of the most dangerous objects in space were created by this single weapons test, and the International Space Station is routinely forced to maneuver to avoid this debris field.[18]

The US responded to China's provocation in 2008 with Operation Burnt Frost, which used a ship-launched SM-3 missile to take down a failed National Reconnaissance Office (NRO) spy satellite designated as USA-193. Because USA-193 was at a much lower altitude and in a decaying orbit, all of the material from the American test safely deorbited and does not present a threat to space transit.[19] The US officially denied that the shootdown was a response to China and asserts that an uncontrolled reentry of the satellite might have presented a threat to people or property.[20]

In 2021, Russia conducted a direct ascent test that created a large debris field and sparked international outrage. Ironically, the test was so dangerous to the crew of the International Space Station that their own cosmonauts sought shelter in their Soyuz capsule and prepared for a possible evacuation.[21]

UNCOOPERATIVE DOCKING, SATELLITE-NAPPING

An alternative to smashing a satellite with a kinetic kill vehicle is to build a sophisticated orbital spacecraft that can pull up and "snatch" an opponent's satellite in space and then either destroy, relocate, or disable it. This snatching process is often called "uncooperative docking," and it has potentially positive dual use applications in space debris removal and satellite servicing. In their excellent book, *Scramble for the Skies*, Dr. Namrata Goswami and Col. Peter Garretson (USAF ret.) describe the behavior of an experimental Chinese satellite, SY-7:

> It suddenly changed course and rendezvoused as close as 100 meters with another satellite. The SY-7's robotic arm, while claimed by China as a science experiment for debris removal simulation, revealed movement and rendezvous maneuvers that could be put to dual use, to include grabbing and destroying an adversary satellite.[22]

The US has semi-secret[ii] spaceplanes called "X–37Bs" that are launched into orbit atop a rocket. These spaceplanes perform mysterious duties with some surprisingly acrobatic orbital maneuvering before returning to land on the runway

---

ii   The hanger they are housed in at Cape Canaveral actually proclaims "Home of the X-37B" in large letters.

built for the Space Shuttles. X-37B missions often last more than a year. Given its on-orbit mobility and payload bay, there has been speculation that the X-37B is capable of performing close inspection or even the capture of adversarial satellites.[23]

As you might expect, seeing the capabilities of the X-37B, China had to have one of their own and built a copycat military spaceplane. Little is known about it, but it is rumored to be very similar in size and design to the US model, though its missions have been far shorter.[24]

DIRECTED ENERGY, AKA DR. EVIL'S SPACE LASERS

Another clean way to deal with enemy satellites is to disable them with directed energy weapons, microwave or laser attacks from the ground or on orbit. China has been targeting American observation satellites for years in an effort to temporarily "dazzle" or permanently blind the CCD imagers in their telescopic cameras.[25] A sufficiently powerful beam can fry the electronics in any satellite without creating a messy debris field. China has built permanent ground stations for this purpose as well as likely deploying mobile sea-and-ground-based systems that would be hard to track or target.[26]

Chinese researchers have published a paper indicating they had developed a relativistic klystron amplifier (RKA) with gigawatts of power in the KA band.[27] These are the same radio frequencies used by many satellites including SpaceX's Starlink satellites. There are conflicting opinions as to whether this power level is sufficient to destroy, disable, or jam US satellites, but at least one Chinese researcher who spoke anonymously to the *South China Morning Post* insists that the device was "overwhelming just to think about" and had the potential to be used as a weapon.[28]

These energy systems can also be turned the other way round to produce a genuine James Bond villain's death ray. In 2022, *South China Morning Post* reported that China has also developed a satellite-based laser weapon capable of firing a hundred times a second for long periods of time and powerful enough that "it could permanently blind humans or vaporise the surface of certain materials." The same article suggests the US is close to launching an even more powerful laser weapon capable of downing hypersonic missiles in flight.[29]

Would anyone use such weapons against another nation's people or vessels? The answer from Beijing appears to be a resounding, "会的!"[iii] In February 2023, *Asia Times* reported that China used military-grade laser weapons against the Philippine Coast Guard, likely in retaliation for the island nation granting the US wider access to its military bases. Sailors aboard the patrol ship at Second Thomas Shoal were temporarily blinded by the high-powered green light.[30]

In the same month, a series of green lights was reported in the skies above Hawaii. Observations by Japan's Subaru Telescope located at the Mauna Kea observatories on the Big Island's peak indicate that the passing Daqi-1 satellite was beaming laser radiation down from what China asserts is a pollution monitoring system.[31]

NUKE THE SITE FROM ORBIT; IT'S THE ONLY WAY TO BE SURE

Another option is to deploy space-based nuclear weapons in convenient orbital inclinations. Such weapons could theoretically be dropped onto American military installations

---

iii "We will!"

or cities with little warning and a limited ability to intercept them. The US relies on satellites with infrared detectors to identify heat signatures from Russian, Chinese, or North Korean ICBMs when these rockets leave the ground.[32] They provide US missile defense operators with a heads-up at the start of the warhead's approximately forty-five-minute flight. Radars on the ground then guide ground-based interceptors (GBI) to the incoming target, preferably near their apogee, outside the atmosphere. Nukes pushed silently out of an orbital platform or maneuvered from their regular orbits might avoid detection and potentially have a shorter delivery time, skipping the high-energy boost phase. They might also come in from inclinations not well covered by our defense systems in Alaska and California. These are pointed to the west, presuming any threat will come across the Pacific from Asia.

To be clear, placing any weapons of mass destruction in orbit is explicitly banned by Article IV of the 1967 Treaty on Principles Governing the Activities of States in the Exploration and Use of Outer Space, including the Moon and Other Celestial Bodies, aka the Outer Space Treaty (OST). Every major spacefaring nation, including the US, China, and Russia, has signed the OST. However, we know that China is the champion of violating treaties, pledges, and commitments. So, keep your eyes wide open and look up.[iv]

---

iv Their violations include commitments under the Genocide Convention for their systematic abuse of Uighur slaves held in concentration camps, a 2014 pledge to halt the sale of human organs from executed prisoners, the 2020 Phase One trade agreements in which China committed to specific goals in the purchase of US products, and a 2015 public commitment not to militarize islands in the South China Sea. See our book, *Death by China*, for a cavalcade of bad Chinese behavior.

HIJACKING CRUISE SHIPS FROM SPACE

Last, but not least, satellite systems are particularly vulnerable to hacking and other forms of cyberattack. For years, military and commercial satellite operators have considered their "exquisite assets" to be unreachable by the hoi polloi, because the knowledge was arcane, and the radio equipment and antennas required to do so were sophisticated, large, and expensive. Because of this (false) confidence in their superior intellect and facilities, space operators routinely failed to implement even the most basic security and encryption protocols, leaving cyber security doors wide open to anyone who could make the connection.

Using less than $500 of easily acquired equipment (like cable TV dish antennas), James Pavur, a Rhodes Scholar studying computer science at the University of Oxford, was able to intercept private communications from geosynchronous communications satellites serving ocean-going vessels in the North Sea and the Mediterranean. In his DPhil viva (PhD dissertation),[v] Dr. Pavur shows that this inexpensive hardware combined with his novel software tool, GSExtract, allowed for the recovery of critical data including passenger manifests and credit card transactions from cruise ships as well as docking schedules and passport data sent ahead to ports by high-end private yachts.[33] Being a "white hat" (good) hacker, Pavur did not retain any of this information and alerted the parties involved of their vulnerabilities as well as providing early results from his work to authorities. The FBI swiftly issued an alert to industry, entitled "VSAT Signals Vul-

---

v   Dr. Autry (coauthor) served as the external examiner for Pavur's viva (dissertation defense) at Oxford.

nerable to Low-Cost Device Exploitation," based on Pavur's warnings.[34]

It turns out that most of the material being transferred by satellite is not encrypted because encryption slows down transmissions that are already suffering from latency; the fifty-thousand-mile round trip to and from these specially placed satellites is what makes the old-school satellite internet so frustratingly unresponsive. In fact, virtual private networks (VPNs) pretty much don't work at all on these channels, and Pavur notes that satellite operators openly advised clients not to use them.[vi]

Pavur was also able to identify more than one thousand vessels in his data as well as the nature of the computing environments on the other end, including operating systems and applications with known vulnerabilities. The identified vessels included governmental vessels, cruise ships, chemical tankers, submarines, fishing fleets, and offshore wind farms.

Pavur did not upload data to live vessels but tested it on his own system aboard a remote vessel. He warns that "we did not interfere with any legitimate uplink connections from vessels as this risked interrupting critical communications and causing harm to end users. Nevertheless, we expect this attack would work equally well for intercepting uplink connections from satellite hosts to the broader internet" and offers the following frightening scenario:

> A terrorist organization which altered nautical charts to cause an oil tanker to run

---

vi   Newer low earth orbit (LEO) constellations like SpaceX's Starlink, OneWeb, and Amazon's Kuiper system do not suffer from this latency issue and offer much more robust data security.

aground on a hidden reef would have a catastrophic environmental impact.

The weaponization of massive ships at sea has significant
political military implications and is right up China's alley of
asymmetric warfare. While we presume military systems are
more robust—Pavur avoided connecting with any of these—
they are not invulnerable and very likely suffer from some
of the same "vulnerability of arrogance" that commercial systems do.

In 2002, John Locker, a satellite enthusiast, attempted to
warn US and Allied commanders that he was able to access
NATO surveillance photos that the military was routing
through commercial satellites. Ignored, he eventually went to
the BBC, which confirmed the breach despite official denials
that the data was insignificant.[35]

Pavur's background work documents that NASA systems
have been compromised on several occasions by hackers, including accessing systems that provided satellite command
and control functions. Some of these attacks were attributed
to Russian and Chinese state-backed efforts. It has been asserted that a US–German–UK science mission, RoSat, may
have been compromised by Russian hackers who infiltrated
control systems at NASA's Goddard Space Flight Center and
destroyed the satellite by pointing its sensors at the Sun.[36]
NASA denies this.

In several cases, hackers have compromised TV satellites
in order to feed their own videos into regular broadcasts.
For instance, Chinese dissidents have been able to insert an-
ti-communist videos into transmissions sent via AsiaSat and
SinoSat on several occasions.[37]

Just before Russia invaded Ukraine in 2022, it launched a cyberattack on Viasat's KA-SAT internet service in the area. In a rare display of governmental transparency on these matters, the US State Department formally confirmed the attack with attribution in a May 10, 2022, statement.[38] American billionaire Elon Musk responded by providing SpaceX Starlink terminals to Ukraine. Russia quickly went after those as well. Musk tweeted that "Starlink has resisted Russian cyberwar jamming & hacking attempts so far, but they're ramping up their efforts."[39] Leaks reveal that the Russian military has been running a specialized cyber-weapons program known as Tobol-1, aimed at disabling the Starlink satellite network.[40]

We hope we have your attention here. There's more scary stuff to come, but we will primarily focus on the exciting story of America's space exploration efforts and the promise that space technology and resources hold for the future of the free world.

LESSONS LEARNED: SPACE MATTERS TODAY

Threats from space are real, immediate, and game-changing. Space technology is changing outcomes on the battlefront today and redefining our possible futures. America cannot afford to put off dealing with space until we solve all those "problems right here on Earth," because space is now one of them. Failure to invest in that now could be catastrophic in a few short years.

If we pay attention, we find that China will often tell us exactly what they intend to do. They intend to dominate the space domain.

It is critical that our leaders keep abreast of what is going on in space and keep our technology and capabilities ahead of our competitors, most particularly China.

CHAPTER NINE

THE VIEW FROM ABOVE: SATELLITES AND OUR PLANET

*We came all this way to explore the moon, and
the most important thing is that we discovered the
Earth.*
—Bill Anders, Apollo 8

A re you sitting in your office looking at rain or snow and wondering what the weather is like on your favorite Caribbean beach? Satellite imagery from the National Oceanic and Atmospheric Administration (NOAA) and commercial companies can answer that. Wondering what it will be like next week or next year? Data collected from satellites and relayed via satellite from hundreds of deep ocean buoys provides the bulk of long-term weather and climate data. Thanks to space technology, we now understand and can track phenomena like El Niño, a periodic warming of South Pacific, which meteorologists use to forecast fishing yields in Peru, corn crops in Mexico, and the bodaciousness of California's snowboarding season.[41]

What about severe weather? Before satellite tracking, blizzards, hurricanes, and tornados slammed into unprepared communities with little warning. The Category 4 storm that destroyed Galveston, Texas, in 1900 killed a quarter of the island's population of thirty-eight thousand, *all* of whom could have been evacuated across bridges to the mainland had space-based storm tracking and communications been available. Today, untold numbers of lives are saved every year when (if) the populace and local governments respond effectively to hurricane, tornado, and wildfire warnings and updates from space.

WOULD YOU LIKE YOUR PLANET FROZEN OR WELL-DONE?

Are you angsty over hyperbole in the climate debate and draconian policy prescriptions? Kids with megaphones, people in masks gluing themselves to things, and Hollywood blockbusters aside, space offers us "just the facts, ma'am" about climate. Space assets, including systems measuring the occultation of GPS signals in the upper atmosphere, enable most of the real data used in long-range climate modeling. A lot of that technology came from NASA systems first designed to explore the climates of Venus, Mars, and other planets in our solar system.[42] Planetary scientists are working to understand how a now frozen Mars lost its atmosphere and warm seas and what natural greenhouse processes turned Earth's twin, Venus, into a burning hellscape. These data are invaluable in understanding how complex planetary climate systems evolve. Space even offers us potential solutions for mitigating drastic climate changes without having to eat crickets or return to the Middle Ages.

Earth has been through many cycles of warming and freezing. Just twenty thousand years ago, not that long in geological time, much of the Northern US including Chicago, Boston, and New York City was crushed under the massive Laurentide Ice Sheet. Sixty-five million years ago, the center of North America was an inland sea, and dinosaurs roamed the forests of an ice-free Antarctica.[43] A global icebox made mammoths happy, and a global sauna was swell for dinos, but most of us like the thermostat where it is currently set.

The geological record shows many circumstances of swift climatic changes, sometimes occurring over mere decades. Just before historical times, those giant ice sheets melted, and rising sea levels burst through the gap between Denmark and Sweden, flooding a shallow freshwater lake and creating the Baltic Sea in about 8,000 BC.[44] The Black Sea may have had a similar origin just a few hundred years later.[45] These real events may be the basis of Great Flood stories in the Bible and other Indo-European cultures. Titanic explorer, Robert Ballard, used underwater robotic vessels to uncover evidence that early human settlements were flooded in what is now the Black Sea off Türkiye.[46]

Regardless of the cause of climatic shifts, *these sorts of violent changes are not conducive to the infrastructure of civilization* that human beings have built over the last couple of thousands of years and that eight billion people now depend on. In the long run, managing the natural variations in our climate is going to be even more important than managing the human impact on it. Fining petrol vehicles driving in central London or covering America's forests and farms with solar panels can't save us from our moody planet.

Ultimately, the Sun drives all of Earth's climate and weather systems. If we could just hang a massive sunshade between the Sun and the Earth to moderate the solar radiation hitting our planet, we might be able to manage ice ages and warming trends. It turns out that there is a set of gravitationally stable points in the Sun and the Earth system where things can indeed "just hang." These are known as Lagrange Points, named for European mathematician Joseph-Louis Lagrange, whose modeling predicted the phenomena.[47] On Christmas Day 2021, a European Ariane 5 rocket launched NASA's huge James Webb Space Telescope (JWST) to Lagrange Point 2 (L2). Everything unfolded as NASA planned, and the JWST now hangs around a stable point one million miles from Earth, delivering stunning images for the public and hordes of valuable data to eager space scientists.

One million miles in the other direction, toward the Sun, the L1 point provides an ideal location to manage sunlight with a fleet of thousands of space umbrellas.[48] Reflectors around L1 could theoretically divert or focus light to cool or warm Earth. While this is literally a very cool idea, it is also the most expensive project ever conceived. For a cheaper alternative, Professor Benjamin Bromley of the University of Utah has recently proposed using dust blasted from the Moon to do the job.[49]

SPACE WEATHER, IT'S A THING

L1 is already providing Earth with useful protection from the Sun. NASA and other space agencies keep a fleet of spacecraft there looking at something they pleasantly call "space weather." It's not always pleasant.

Recall our opening chapter and the threat of a Chinese EMP attack from space disrupting our digitally dependent lives. It turns out we had a taste of that way back in the nineteenth century.

On September 1, 1859, British scientist Christopher Carrington recorded a massive disruption on the surface of the Sun. This coronal mass ejection (CME), or solar flare, launched a massive wave of highly charged particles toward Earth. Eighteen hours later, these atomic nuclei began impacting Earth's upper atmosphere causing the most brilliant northern and southern lights ever observed. In fact, the aurora became visible around the globe, and the skies above Hawaii were indeed filled with space rainbows. Although the electronics of the age were even more primitive than those affected by the 1962 tests, the storm was certainly noticed. NASA scientist James Green noted, "A significant portion of the world's 200,000 km of telegraph lines were adversely affected, many of which were unusable for 8 hours or more, which had a real economic impact."[50]

On March 13, 1989—known in Quebec, Canada as "The Day the Sun Brought Darkness"—a solar flare took down Quebec's power grid for more than nine hours.[51] Outages were also reported in the northeast US, and radio systems around the world were knocked off the air.

If the Carrington Event or even a CME of half its strength occurred today, the sunward-facing portion of the globe would be digitally disabled, and their electrical grids would be down, perhaps for good. The odds of such a storm hitting in the next ten years are probably between one in two hundred and one in fifty. The odds of such a half-strength Carrington Event occurring in a century are extremely concerning. The disruption might create confusion or provide a pretext for war. During the 1989 event, it was originally presumed that the Soviet Union was jamming the signals of Radio Free Europe. How might a nuclear power on the unlucky side of the globe act, knowing that they were about to be laid low and left at the mercy of their geopolitical rivals?

The Deep Space Climate Observatory (DSCOVR) and the Advanced Composition Explorer (ACE) operated by NOAA and NASA watch the Sun from L1. When the bad day comes, they will radio a warning to Earth, giving us twenty to sixty minutes to prepare. This is adequate time for many critical governmental, military, and commercial systems to be powered down and sensitive gear secured inside Faraday cages, metal mesh boxes that protect sensitive equipment from electrical charges. Political leaders will be able to communicate assurances to their allies and rivals, and emergency assistance could be initiated. The public will have some warning to gather their candles and stick their phones into a metal box. You can actually buy a EMP/CME protection bag on Amazon for fifty bucks, though odds are that it is probably made in China.

DSCOVR and ACE are slated to be augmented/replaced by NOAA's Space Weather Follow On-Lagrange 1 (SWFO-L1) satellite in 2025. The European Space Agency also provides space weather data from its Solar and Heliospheric Observatory (SOHO). ESA is planning to launch a pair of space weather observers called Vigil to L1 and L5.

T-REX AND THE TERRIBLE, HORRIBLE, NO GOOD, VERY BAD DAY

Returning to those dinosaurs roaming the long Antarctic night, they might still be running things if only they had invested in a decent space program. The two-hundred-million-year reign of the terrible lizards came to an end when a large asteroid smacked into Mexico's Yucatan Peninsula.[52] This impact produced an explosion a billion times more powerful than the atomic bomb that destroyed Hiroshima in 1945. A crater hundreds of miles across and a mountain range taller than Mount Everest were created. Professor Joanna Morgan of Imperial College London told the BBC, "This all happens on the scale of minutes, which is quite amazing."[53]

While the impact immediately sterilized nearly everything within a few thousand miles, it also ejected megatons of the Earth's crust into space, which then reentered at hypersonic speeds barbecuing triceratops by the millions and setting off massive forest fires around the world. Added to this were massive amounts of sulfur and other vaporized minerals.[54] Earth's atmosphere was likely choked with smoke haze for many years, resulting in rapid global cooling that rendered the climate incompatible with most of the surviving life forms.[55] Smaller animals that were burrowing underground—our mammalian ancestors—eventually emerged to repopulate the world.

The dino-apocalypse was not a one-off event. Impacts like this have occurred many times in Earth's history and are also tied to other massive extinction events. In fact, there is a theory, known as the Shiva Hypothesis, that asserts the nature of our sun's movement through the galaxy results in material from the distant Oort Cloud being hurled into the inner solar system approximately once every twenty-seven million years.[56] A similar theory blames an undetected super-planet or brown dwarf star named "Nemesis" that may be in orbit around our own system.[57]

If you feel that asteroids aren't something that we seriously need to worry about, we've got news for you. In February 2013, a ten-thousand-ton asteroid fragment skimmed Earth's atmosphere and exploded over the southern Russian city of Chelyabinsk.[58] The explosion was comparable to a high-altitude nuclear blast and set off nuclear weapons detectors around the world. Fifteen hundred people were injured, and thousands of buildings were reported as damaged.[59] If the arrival of this space rock had varied by just a fraction of a second, Earth's movement would have shifted the impact site. It could have destroyed Moscow, killed millions, and induced political chaos into an already paranoid nuclear power. If the asteroid had smacked into the Sea of Japan, it might have created a catastrophic tidal wave inundating hundreds of coastal cities. A 1908 impact in Siberia yielded a twelve-megaton explosion that flattened eighty million large trees in a sparsely populated forest. If such a thing ever occurs over Los Angeles, Shanghai, or Istanbul, tens of millions of people will perish.[60]

PLANETARY DEFENSE IS A REAL THING

Is there some way humankind can avoid the fate of our stegosaurus predecessors and protect our cities? The effort to keep our world from being abruptly crushed by a rock from space is known as "planetary defense." There are two major components to planetary defense: locating and tracking potentially dangerous objects in space and diverting them from striking Earth. Polls consistently show that a majority of Americans believe this effort should be a top priority for NASA.[61] Our space agency is on it! NASA and several global organizations are busy searching for near Earth objects (NEOs) that may present a danger in the future.

As part of a broader international effort called Space-guard, the US Congress mandated NASA to catalogue 90 percent of NEOs larger than one kilometer.[62] That mandate was completed in 2011, but the hunt continues. NASA's Planetary Defense Coordination Office (PDCO) supports the Catalina Sky Survey (CSS) run by the University of Arizona out of the Lunar and Planetary Lab in Tucson.[63] CSS has discovered several small asteroids *before* they grazed Earth's atmosphere, including one that lit up the skies over Toronto during the predawn hours of November 19, 2022.[64]

NASA also funds the University of Hawaii's Asteroid Terrestrial-impact Last Alert System (ATLAS), which is always on the lookout for incoming objects that might have been missed by other surveys. ATLAS's automated telescopes take advantage of the optimal astronomical conditions on the tall mountains of Maui and the Big Island to provide a few days warning of an impending strike. In 2022, telescopes were added in Chile and South Africa for southern sky coverage.

The Panoramic Survey Telescope and Rapid Response System (Pan-STARRS) is a sky survey instrument funded by the US Air Force and operated by the University of Hawaii.[65] While its primary mission is to search for NEOs, Pan-STARRS surprised the world in October of 2017 by catching the first interstellar visitor to our solar system. This object, 'Oumuamua, behaved very oddly. Coming into our system at a very high speed, it made a really neat swing around the Sun. This maneuver looked very similar to the sort of gravitational slingshot that NASA deep-space probes often use: a flyby of one planet to redirect their flights and gain speed for travel to a further destination. 'Oumuamua then *accelerated* on its way out of our system. Though this was likely caused by natural events, serious scientists have entertained the possibility that 'Oumuamua was an alien starship using our star as a round-about on its long journey through the galaxy.[66] Efforts are underway to be able to launch a quick intercept mission that could rendezvous with our next interstellar visitor.

The B612 Foundation,[i] an NGO, also does very serious work on the topic including supporting an open-source software platform for mapping the objects in our solar system.[67]

IT'S LIKE *ARMAGEDDON*, BUT WITHOUT BRUCE WILLIS

Identifying an incoming city-busting or even civilization-ending asteroid is one thing. Doing something about it is another. The real world is not a Michael Bay movie, and Bruce Willis is not going to learn to fly a Space Shuttle in a few days and nuke the offending space rock. If we could blow up an asteroid, it would most likely create a field of just-as-deadly meteors still headed in our direction. The best plan is likely to deflect the asteroid's course away from our delicate planet.

NASA's Planetary Defense Coordination Office funded a project called the Double Asteroid Redirect Test (DART). On September 26, 2022, the 1,300-pound DART spacecraft intentionally collided with Dimorphos, a small moon orbiting a near-Earth asteroid named "Didymos." NASA chose this "double asteroid" system so that any resulting change in the trajectory of the smaller rock could be easily observed via changes in its orbit around its larger partner. The results were spectacular. Telescopes witnessed the explosion of material ejected from Dimorphos, and the little moon's orbit shifted

---

i   B612 is named for the minor planet that was home to a young man and a rose in Antoine de Saint-Exupéry's classic work, *Le Petit Prince*.

noticeably. Images produced by the Hubble space telescope in 2023 revealed a collection of objects following the asteroid pair. These were presumably loose boulders knocked off the surface of Dimorphos by the impact.

DART showed us that we can change the trajectory of an asteroid but that we also need to be careful with ensuring all the pieces are headed in a safe direction. NASA administrator Bill Nelson remarked, "This is a watershed moment for planetary defense and all of humanity, demonstrating commitment from NASA's exceptional team and partners from around the world."[68]

Speaking of international partners, planetary defense is one area where engagement in space with China might actually be constructive. As former Senator Nelson noted, "All of us have a responsibility to protect our home planet. After all, it's the only one we have." While we may not agree about most anything else, preventing the surface of Earth from being vaporized by rocks from space is something that transcends political ideology and economic competition.

Science fiction writers have hypothesized that asteroids could be weaponized via a malicious diversion. However, that would make for an extremely unwieldy weapon that could not be timed. As noted earlier, the Boys from Beijing have a plethora of more practical technologies with which to do us in. Having more telescopes monitoring NEOs, shared data, more launch capacity for intercepting them, and additional ideas for diverting them is probably a good idea, regardless of the source.

LESSONS LEARNED: SPACE MATTERS TOMORROW

Continued investment in space science is critical. Natural threats from space can be existential ones, and understanding our space environment and eventually developing the ability to manage it could be as important as maintaining military superiority or commercial dominance in space.

Funding for NASA's Science Mission Directorate must not be gutted to support human space exploration or any other programmatic priorities.

A few areas, including pure science and planetary defense, offer opportunities to constructively engage our adversaries.

CHAPTER EIGHT

THE FUTURE'S SO BRIGHT: SPACE DELIVERS THE GOODS

*All this knowledge harvested in orbit will
have, sooner or later, an impact on our
daily lives. I believe fundamental research in
space can make the world a better place.*
—Leonardo Surdo, bioengineer,
European Space Agency

In economics, an externality is some outcome that is unaccounted for in the model; it is an unintended byproduct of a business activity or policy. A negative externality is an undesired outcome, such as air or water pollution associated with some manufacturing process. A positive externality is a happy coincidence, such as discovering that the waste product from the factory has a valuable application. Plastics were a positive externality created from the waste of refining petroleum into gasoline during the automotive boom of the last century.

PLEASANTLY SURPRISED BY SPIN-OFFS

Much of our computing technology is a positive externality of US governmental space projects. In 1962, Bob Taylor moved from NASA's Office of Advanced Research and Technology to the Department of Defense's Advanced Research Projects Agency (ARPA). He led the development of several important computing technologies. These include the ubiquitous pointing device we call a mouse. In 1966, Taylor convinced ARPA's director, Charles M. Herzfeld, to allocate $1 million from an ICBM defense program to his idea of connecting multiple computers together on a network. In 1969, a message was sent across this ARPAnet between a computer at UCLA and one at Stanford.[69] The internet was born, thanks to the Cold War space race! Taylor went on to lead a famed research team at Xerox's Palo Alto Research Center (PARC) that developed the graphical user interface (GUI), local area network (LAN), and most of what we consider modern computing.[70]

Many people are aware that NASA has a brag list of "spin-offs" including: portable power tools, medical telemetry, the memory foam mattress, tankless water heaters, air cleaners, and freeze-dried foods.[71] NASA and DoD space efforts also drove the development of the solar panels and fuel cells essential to today's "green energy" boom.[72] The efficient blade design on modern wind turbines is also the outcome of NASA aeronautical R & D.[73]

The United States Space Force manages a constellation of satellites, the Global Positioning System (GPS), designed to provide location and timing information. GPS is now ubiquitous in our daily commutes, saving time and fuel. It recovers lost property, solves crime, and saves lives.[74] It also optimizes the routes of millions of commercial trucks, ships, and planes, saving billions in fuel costs and reducing local pollution and global emissions. GPS also serves as the world's clock, providing free timing accurate to fourteen nanoseconds to everyone on Earth. Manufacturers use the signal to time the handoffs between robotic systems in today's high-tech factories. Stock, bond, and commodity exchanges use GPS to time all our online trades in microseconds. A 2019 study by RTI International determined that GPS has provided over $1.4 trillion in value to the United States, and that system was worth at least $1 billion a day to the American economy.[75] A 2008 Motorola study determined that the return to America's long-haul trucking fleet was $53 billion a year, more than enough to pay for all our nation's space expenditures.[76] Of course, the rest of the world has been getting a free ride, saving trillions of dollars courtesy of the US space program. And, if you track such things, you might want to ask someone, "Where the hell are America's 'carbon credits' for all those emission reductions?"

LET'S PLAY *WHERE'S WALDO*, ON A GLOBAL SCALE

Imagine that you are relaxing on a cruise ship in the Aegean Sea. A message pops up on your phone (via the ship's connection to the Starlink satellite constellation) informing you that an earthquake has just occurred near your home in Southern California at the same time a rare hurricane is battering the region. This actually happened to one of us (Autry) during the summer of 2023. A quick glance at the satellite view from Google Maps suggests that everything is fine! In fact, it looks like a bright, cloudless, sunny day, even though it is nighttime in the region! That's because those photos were taken months ago.[i]

Until recently, satellite images of Earth were either low resolution, meaning they don't provide much fine detail, or low cadence, meaning they were taken only occasionally. You couldn't have both a good and a timely picture. Years ago, Google chose good over timely and has been offering fairly high-resolution pictures that are far from current. These pics are often captured by satellites traveling in sun-synchronous, polar orbits, meaning they travel north to south around Earth with just the right timing so that they can pass over the same spots each day at the same time. Such satellites are usually at an altitude of about 600 to 800 km,[77] which is a fairly low (or close to the ground) orbit. Theoretically, Google could access images daily and update them. They don't do this for several reasons including that they want photos taken during optimal (cloud-free) days, and each data update costs money.

On the other hand, if you go to the NOAA GEOS Image viewer site,[ii] you will find pictures of your region taken every few hours! It's great if you want to see the weather patterns, and this is how we track those hurricanes and other atmospheric phenomena that might ruin your Caribbean vacation. However, these images are useless if you want to see your home. GEOS, or geostationary Earth observation satellites, are in very special orbits that sit right above the equator at

---

i   To see more about the image in Google Maps, hover your mouse over the area and look at the bottom status bar. It may (or may not) show you when the image was taken and by what agency or satellite. Using the company's Google Earth app provides more robust capabilities and information on the data sources.

ii   Found at: https://www.star.nesdis.noaa.gov/GOES/index.php.

an altitude of 22,236 miles. At that particular altitude, the satellite is traveling with the same orbital velocity as Earth's rotational speed, and it will orbit Earth once every day. The result is that it appears to hang in space directly over one spot on Earth. Even with a really amazing telescopic lens, these satellites can't zoom in very well from that distance. They take pictures of whole continents at a time, and even cities are mostly invisible at this resolution.

If we want to get closer to Earth, the satellite must move faster relative to Earth's surface. Being closer, they also capture smaller area. This makes it impossible to get timely pictures of the same spot without a whole lot of satellites, like hundreds of them. Until very recently, the cost of imaging satellites ranged from $100 million to several billions, and space launches cost hundreds of millions a pop. So, nobody was going to fund constellations of satellites required to image the entire planet in a timely manner. All that has changed in the last decade, with the ascendance of commercial space. With government stepping aside to allow for a competitive, market-driven space economy, the price of space hardware and launch has been dropping exponentially. Satellites are now being built for hundreds of thousands of dollars and launched for less than $1 million each. This has allowed new companies like Planet and BlackSky, as well as incumbent firms like Maxar, to begin to build those imaging constellations. As of this writing, Planet has 150 satellites in orbit, collecting 1,300 daily images of every location on Earth's surface.[78]

OK, you can see your house when you need to. How is that a revolution? When Russian forces invaded Ukraine in February of 2022, many people assumed that larger nation's technological advantages, including its renowned space capabilities, would give Putin a decisive victory. That did not turn out to be the case, and one of those reasons was because commercial imaging data provided the Ukrainian military battlefield information at least as good and probably better than what Russian commanders were getting from their state-operated assets. Publicly available satellite images of Russia's massive troop buildup along the Ukrainian border brought the impending war into the public eye,[79] and a bird's-eye view of the tank columns and smoldering Ukrainian cities proved to be powerful tools in the hands of a news media drumming up support for Zelenskyy's underdog army. Maxar was even able to quickly deploy additional satellites to cover Ukraine.[80] It could be argued that commercial space tipped the balance of a war and shifted the global perception of it as well.

The range of human color vision is not the limit of the electromagnetic spectrum. Satellites are equipped to view Earth in ultraviolet, infrared, and with radar as well. We call this broader class of scanning satellites "remote sensing," and it offers many commercial benefits. Agricultural yields can be improved by observing the crops in multiple spectrums to detect pests and diseases.[81] Scans in infrared and other frequencies also help optimize irrigation by showing the distribution of water in the fields, information of immense value in arid but highly productive farming regions like California and Israel.[82] Insurers are also using these systems to analyze risk, foresee claims, and verify claims.[83] Insurers are using high-cadence satellite data to answer questions like, "Did the house burn during the wildfire, or was the blaze set afterwards?"

Of course, combing through millions of pixels of data taken dozens of times a day from thousands of satellites is a Herculean task. Applying AI to high-cadence imaging data is where the money is in today's space world. Computers are scanning all those fields of crops and distilling what they see into actionable data to the farmers. An algorithm can be trained to identify vehicles or cargo containers and track them from their source to their destination, information that can be invaluable for the shipper, the receiver, their competitors, and the customs agents.

Satellites using synthetic aperture radar (SAR) are able to scan every major oil storage facility on Earth and determine what is in those big, round holding tanks. Using this information, a company called "Ursa Space" produces reports on global, national, and corporate petroleum holdings each day.[84] That's valuable information for traders and diplomats alike. Even better SAR sats can be used to detect oil spills at sea so they can be stopped and cleaned up faster.[85] SAR sats can also see where optical satellites cannot. Radar can cut through clouds and provide data *at night* about a variety of on-the-ground activities. Some satellites are even equipped with ground-penetrating radar to see what is under the surface. NASA has used this to locate lost archaeological sites.[86] Imagine what else could be found with such a capability.

Every technology brings its downside, and the benefits of Earth imaging are complicated by issues of privacy. It might be imagined that the police would love to use this technology to track bad guys, and divorce lawyers might be very interested in where a particular spouse's car was on any given night. Of course, bad guys can be smart too. Imagine being able to know where all the police cars in a city were at any given time or observe the route of a fleet of armored cars making cash pickups. Tracking the private yachts of the world's wealthiest people would be no problem. NOAA regulations have restricted remote sensing operations to protect national security assets and to some degree, your privacy. In fact, when Elon Musk launched his Tesla Roadster and took a picture of it with Earth in the background, he ran afoul of NOAA by not getting an imaging license.[87] Look for these privacy and security issues to be front and center on your news feed in coming years.

WHAT IS SEEN AND WHAT IS NOT SEEN

Of course, there are some folks who have zero respect for your or anyone else's privacy. Our friends in Beijing's Ministry of State Security are eager to harness the power of high-cadence, high-resolution satellite imaging. The Chinese police state is built on data, and the more the better—not just data on folks in China but yours as well. China maintains a massive database of documents on millions of regular Americans and via state-sponsored hacking may have your credit card statements and your family's medical records on their servers. Knowing where you have been and with whom is just one more data point that may come in handy should they ever desire to elicit your services or compromise your kin with threats or blackmail. Chinese AI is combing through all of this information and producing a web of targets for their massive spy network to exploit.[88]

I'M IN ANTARCTICA, CAN YOU HEAR ME NOW?

Collecting data isn't enough; you've got to be able to distribute it! If the boom in imaging satellites surprises you, you'll be utterly amazed at what is going on in communications. At the start of the last decade, there were approximately one thousand operational satellites in orbit. As of this writing, there are ten thousand, and more than half of these are from Elon Musk's Starlink constellation.

If you've used satellite-based internet from a remote location, on a ship at sea, or on an airplane, you've likely experienced the frustration of slow responses. You click on something on a web page, and it seems to take an interminable amount of time for the response. It seems slow, and yet it is possible to stream high-resolution video from these same satellites. What gives? You have just run up against the limitations of the speed of light! Seriously. The satellite you were communicating with is in a geostationary orbit more than twenty thousand miles above Earth's equator. Even at 186,000 miles per second, it actually takes a noticeable fraction of a second for your "mouse down" request to get to the satellite and then back down to a ground station near the server you are communicating with. That server responds to your computer with a similar delay. Sometimes there are several back-and-forth communications before the next page is displayed. Even if the data itself is moving at a high bandwidth, this latency is unavoidable. That makes traditional satellite communications unacceptable for a variety of applications where microseconds matter, including high-speed commodities trading, remote control of vehicles, and most notably, video games. Log onto *Halo* or *Call of Duty* with a satellite connection, and your character will be dead at least a second before you even know what happened.

Musk's Starlink, on the other hand, provides broadband, low-latency internet connections to people all over the world by using the same strategy Planet applied to imaging. Starlink has small, inexpensive satellites in very low orbits. Being just a couple of hundred miles up, the latency is gone. The challenge is that these low orbits move very quickly over Earth, being above a particular location for only a few minutes at a time. This requires the Starlink constellation to have literally thousands of satellites. Musk has been launching these satellites in sets of sixty, a couple times per week, and has stated he may launch as many as forty thousand of them![89]

And Musk isn't alone. OneWeb, a UK–Europe–India partnership, has a constellation of 648 internet satellites. OneWeb was founded by American tech entrepreneur Greg Wyler and initially secured funding from Richard Branson and Qualcomm to begin manufacturing in Florida. When the venture faced bankruptcy in 2020, China maneuvered to gain control of the company.[90] To prevent that, the UK government entered an agreement with Indian billionaire Sunil Mittal to buy the operation.[91] Japan's SoftBank also has a share. Since then, French-based Eutelsat also invested. This has been concerning to the intelligence community, as Eutelsat is heavily backed by China's sovereign wealth fund.[92]

Amazon's Jeff Bezos is also preparing to launch his own internet constellation called "Kuiper." The company has received permission from the FCC to launch over three thousand satellites.[93] Kuiper has been awaiting launch capability from Bezos's rocket startup, Blue Origin, and/or the new Vulcan rocket from United Launch Alliance. Because of delays in those launchers, Amazon recently made a deal with SpaceX to launch several of their satellites.[94]

Starlink, OneWeb, and Kuiper all require bulky receivers and antennas roughly the size of a pizza box, making them transportable rather than portable. You can't put this in your pocket. Not to fear, Virginia-based startup Lynk has your phone covered, anywhere. Lynk's constellation of satellites will provide direct connections from your standard Apple or Android mobile phone anywhere on Earth.[95] The connection is low latency but not high bandwidth. It's optimized for text and apps and can support voice but not video. That's still more than enough for many locations in sub-Saharan Africa, Latin America, and Oceania that have been off the grid. The firm initiated its service in the island nation of Palau in 2023.[96] Lynk was founded by Charles Miller, a serial space entrepreneur and former senior advisor for commercial space. Miller coined the term "New Space" to define the phenomena of entrepreneurial space endeavors.[97]

LESSONS LEARNED: SPACE IS TRANSFORMING OUR WORLD, TODAY

The benefits from space are not all found in *Star Trek*'s twenty-third century. Our national investments in space have been a major source of America's competitive advantage.

We must continue to fund space science, exploration, and development not because we know what the returns will be but because we do not know how we will benefit.

National industrial policy should encourage entrepreneurship and private investment in space technologies to leverage the fundamental research that NASA constantly generates for America's benefit.

CHAPTER SEVEN

THE CORNUCOPIA OF THE HEAVENS: SPACE RESOURCES AND DEVELOPMENT

There is a tide in the affairs of men, which taken at
the flood leads on to fortune; omitted, all the voyage
of their life is bound in shallow and miseries.
—William Shakespeare[i]

In 1957, the International Geophysical Year (IGY), America saw a future driven by the benefits of science and engineering. Nuclear and solar would provide unlimited clean power for a coming flood of labor-saving appliances. Semiconductors would usher in a new era of "transistorized" electronic gadgets. Monsanto's agricultural technology was revolutionizing food production, and DuPont promised us "better living through chemistry." Sci-fi movies in 3D were the fad. NASA was founded that year, and space was about to open the planets to human exploration. Automobiles reflected this futurism with outlandish fins and rocket exhaust taillights. By 1961, the

i   Brutus in *Julius Caesar*

future was so bright, our young president had to wear shades as he stared up at the space agency's shiny new rockets.

Yet, by the 1970s, the world was about to end. A lot of very smart people and prestigious organizations such as The Club of Rome assured us that we had reached the *Limits to Growth* as our population grew and Earth's resources became scarcer.[98] Oil was sure to run out soon. Nuclear power was an existential threat. Our chemical saviors seemed to all be carcinogenic, and modern agriculture would exterminate life as we knew it within a few years. The pollution from our rocket-inspired cars appeared to be inducing a new global ice age,[99] or then again, maybe it would roast us all.[100] The popular 1973 film *Soylent Green* showed us the hellish future of 2022. Edward G. Robinson chose a pleasant death over another day peddling a bike for power while Charlton Heston revealed that we were living on green crackers made from the euthanized corpses of his fellow citizens. Bottom line, there was no way the world could support a population of four billion souls.

So, where is the doomsday *Soylent Green* promised us? While many of us harbor serious misgivings about the state of our world, and "smart people" continue to warn of looming environmental catastrophes, we are not peddling for power or eating our dead. Since the Reverend Malthus laid out the basic idea of resource peaking more than two hundred years ago, would-be prophets of doom have always failed to account for the heroic capacity of technologists and entrepreneurs to overcome challenges and avert disasters, even the ones they have created.

The US and the USSR each planned to launch their first artificial satellite during the IGY. The Soviets succeeded with

Sputnik in October of 1957, while American efforts floundered until January 1958. Both of these spacecrafts rode modified military rockets to space. A hidden irony of Russia's early space triumphs was that they had been compelled to build more capable rockets because their crude nuclear warheads were so much larger than America's more refined nukes. The good news is that the Cold War competition drove both countries to produce relatively reliable orbital rockets, a positive externality that has provided a cornucopia of unexpected benefits for everyone on Earth.

THE MOON MAY NOT BE MADE OF GREEN CHEESE, BUT JUST LOOK AT ALL THAT CHEDDAR!

In our 2011 book, *Death by China*, we detailed the brilliant mercantilist strategies that China used to gain a global monopoly over the production of rare earth elements. Primarily through a willingness to despoil its own environment, the communist nation now controls more than 90 percent of the world's supply of metals.[101] Little-known rare earths like yttrium and neodymium are critical to maintaining your tech-enabled lifestyle as well as America's tech-dependent military. If you think having everything from the avionics in our ICBMs to the computers in our tanks dependent on our top adversary looks like a losing strategy, you'd be right. How about titanium? You know, the super-strong, super-light metal used in hypersonic missiles, desalination systems, and artificial hip joints? Titanium dioxide even makes the powder on your donuts brilliantly white. Unfortunately, China is now the world's largest producer of titanium, and much of the rest comes from difficult places like Russia, Ukraine, and Kazakhstan. The US produces almost none. In order to build America's SR-71 Blackbird spy planes, the CIA set up fake machine shops in Europe as fronts to buy up Soviet titanium and then shipped it to Lockheed's Skunk Works plant in Palmdale, California.[102]

What can we do when the global supply chain won't co-operate? It turns out that all these metals, along with more mundane things like iron and gold, are abundant on asteroids and likely in asteroid impact craters on the surface of the Moon. For example, there may be more platinum group metals on the asteroid Psyche than have been mined in all of human history on Earth. The market value of this space rock has been estimated at ten quintillion dollars, or about six hundred thousand times the annual economic activity of the US.[ii] Of course, that valuation is dependent on being able to retrieve this material and ignores the laws of economics. Psyche is in an orbit between Mars and Jupiter, millions of miles from Earth and travelling at tens of thousands of miles per hour. Could we even get to it? Actually, NASA launched a probe to Psyche in October of 2023. When it arrives there in August of 2029, we may find a space gold mine or just do some amazing planetary science. NASA's principal investigator on the project, Lindy Elkins-Tanton of Arizona State University, notes that "we won't know anything for sure until we get there. We wanted to ask primary questions about the material that built planets. We're filled with questions and not a lot of answers. This is real exploration."[103]

DILITHIUM CRYSTALS, UNOBTANIUM, HELIUM-3

The best news about mining the Moon and asteroids is that these appear to be entirely lifeless rocks. Extracting and processing these metals in space spares our own planet's precious

---

ii   A quintillion dollars is a million trillion dollars.

biosphere from the destruction and pollution created by terrestrial mining and refining without impacting any other life forms.

In sci-fi movies, space yields up amazing materials like the dilithium crystals that power the Starship Enterprise across the galaxy and the unobtanium found only on Pandora. While these materials are indeed entirely fictional, there may actually be a magical Moon mineral that could transform all our lives here on Earth. A unique variety of helium, the isotope with just one neutron, helium-3 (He-3), may hold the promise of unlimited, clean energy by enabling nuclear fusion reactions that do not generate residual radiation in the surrounding reactor material. He-3 also has applications in neutron detection, MRI imaging, and cryogenic research.[104]

He-3 is extremely rare on Earth and very hard to access, and there is no hope of producing enough to run commercial fusion reactors. While the Sun's own nuclear furnace is continually throwing off relatively large amounts of He-3, virtually none of it makes it to the surface of our planet due to our magnetosphere and atmosphere. He-3 is likely to be found in the lunar regolith (Moon dirt). Former CIA analyst and army intelligence officer Tim Chrisman has said, "Outer space holds virtually limitless amounts of energy and raw materials, from Helium-3 fuel on the Moon for clean fusion reactors to heavy metals and volatile gases from asteroids, which can be harvested for use on Earth and in space."[105]

While there is serious debate about using He-3 in reactors, and the idea of mining this material and returning it to Earth remains science fiction in the West, China is all over the idea. China's Change 1 lunar probe was tasked with detecting He-3, and it appears to have been very successful at that.[106]

The head of China's lunar program, Ouyang Ziyuan, has said that the Moon is so rich in He-3 that it could solve humanity's energy problems for at least ten thousand years.[107] Chrisman adds, "China will almost certainly use any resources it is able to acquire to the detriment of its adversaries, competitors and bystanders alike."[108]

IT'S THE WATER

While exotic materials like Helium-3 are intriguing, it turns out the humblest of substances is the one most likely to drive a space economy, namely water. Water is, in itself, essential to life. Water is also a source of oxygen, the only thing that is even more essential. Splitting each atom of oxygen out of our H_2O, we also get hydrogen ($2H_2O \rightarrow 2H_2 + O_2$), which happens to be an excellent rocket fuel. Burning that hydrogen fuel with the oxygen can get you anywhere in the solar system. With the water and the oxygen, the only other indispensable consumable an occupied spacecraft or station requires is food. Producing food in space also depends on water. This brings us to the question, "Where can we find water in space?"

It turns out there is a whole lot of water in space. Comets are mostly big balls of ice that normally orbit far out beyond Pluto in the distant frozen area called the Oort Cloud. Gravitational disturbances occasionally fling them into the inner solar system, where the Sun boils water off their surfaces and gives them the lovely tails we are familiar with. Most of the water on Earth arrived from comets impacting our planet. These comet-planet collisions are common enough that scientists actually caught one in July of 1994, when the newly discovered comet Shoemaker-Levy 9 crashed into Jupiter. It left very visible scars on that planet's dense atmosphere.[109] Comets have also deposited water onto the larger moons of the big gas giant planets. Europa, a moon of Jupiter, is covered with a deep saltwater sea containing twice as much water as all the oceans of Earth.[110] This makes it a very interesting place to look for life, and NASA's Europa Clipper mission will head there in 2024 and arrive in 2030.

Europa's sea is unfortunately covered by miles of ice, and the moon itself is millions of miles away and swathed in powerful radiation concentrated by Jupiter's powerful magnetosphere. It's not an attractive well for space settlers in the near future. The good news is that a reasonable amount of water appears to be available on our own Moon in the form of ice trapped at the bottom of permanently shaded craters near the lunar poles. NASA and the Indian Space Research Organization (ISRO) have worked together to prove the existence of Moon water. In 2008, Chandrayaan-1 used a NASA-provided instrument to see this water in infrared light, and in 2009, NASA intentionally crashed a rocket stage into a crater near the Moon's south pole and then flew the Lunar Crater Observation and Sensing Satellite (LCROSS) probe into the debris plume generated by that impact. Water was detected in abundance.[111]

Why should we care if there is water on the Moon? With the current generation of rockets and spacecraft, it costs tens of thousands of dollars to deliver a liter of water to the International Space Station. Hauling water to the Moon could cost millions. These outrageous transportation costs are why the astronauts on the ISS recycle everything. During a White House to Space Station phone call in April of 2017, President Donald Trump asked astronaut Peggy Whitson, "What are we learning by being in space?" Whitson offered the president examples of how precious resources were conserved on the ISS, including recycling the air and water. She added, "Water is such a precious resource up here that we also are cleaning up our urine and making it drinkable." The president responded with a wry smile, "Well, that's good. I'm glad to hear that. Better you than me."[112]

All joking aside, the value of any water already in space is very clear, and it is already driving an "ice rush" on the Moon with Russia, India, Israel, Japan, and the US all planning missions to the Moon's southern regions in the last few years. China's lander is already there.

MAKING IT IN SPACE

Developing space not only offers us the chance to extract resources without fouling our precious planet but also promises to be the factory floor of the future. Space provides us with a unique environment that offers some advantages over Earth. First among these is the lack of gravity.

Why is the zero-g world a good place to make things? Picture a pharmaceutical factory on Earth. What do you see? A great deal of the floor space will be filled with mixing vats and chemical reactors that require rotation, stirring, vibration, or other systems to keep those medical molecules thoroughly mixed in solution so that the correct lifesaving compounds can be formed. This mixing dilemma is primarily an artifact of gravity. Inside Earth's "gravity well," everything is being pulled down with a constant acceleration of one g. Heavier atoms and molecules fall "out of solution" and accumulate on the bottom of vats while the lighter elements float to the top.

Anytime you open a can of paint, you'll see that effect and must either shake the can vigorously or get out your stir stick to remedy it. In the "microgravity" environment of a space station, your buttercup yellow enamel or new chemotherapy drug will stay perfectly mixed.

The rising of warmer molecules to the surface of liquids also creates undesirable imperfections in solidifying materials. Gravity is so annoying to chemistry that there are molecules, compounds, and materials that cannot form at all in our one-g environment but that could be produced in microgravity. Some of these may have extraordinarily valuable properties. There are drugs and molecules in this category that medical researchers are very interested in. These include potentially revolutionary treatments for cancer.[113] R & D conducted in zero gravity also promises potential breakthroughs for Alzheimer's and other deadly conditions.[114]

The improved uniformity of crystal growth in space also promises improved drug delivery and storage. This could change a multi-hour infusion process into a simple shot. Crystallizing vaccines and proteins could extend the shelf life of drugs by years,[115] saving billions of dollars at home as well as millions of lives in the developing world where refrigeration is unreliable. A 2019 survey by BMI/Fitch Group reported that 60 percent of pharmaceutical company executives believed that the space economy would significantly impact their sector in the coming decades.[116]

Perfect formation of crystal and glass in microgravity offers improvements in laser and fiber-optic technologies. Perfect crystals can increase the performance of high-powered lasers used in everything from fusion power systems to weapons. These crystals may be worth millions of dollars per kilogram.[117] A special type of optical fiber called "ZBLAN" promises to revolutionize data transmission by allowing multispectral lasers on a single cable. Making ZBLAN on Earth is difficult because gravity induces the formation of bubble and crystal structures that impede the transmission of light signals. NASA has been helping private companies, like Flawless Photonics, test the production of ZBLAN cable in microgravity on the ISS.[118] This cable can sell for hundreds of dollars per meter, and there is a market for thousands of kilometers of ZBLAN cables, including trans-oceanic runs.[119]

Crystals are also the basis for solar panels as well as the semiconductors in integrated circuits and microprocessors. Crystals grow more perfectly without gravity distorting them. Additionally, Stanford University and others are seeking to improve the quality of terrestrially produced semiconductor crystals by reheating them and allowing them to reform more perfectly in microgravity, a process called "annealing."[120] Better crystal formation promises to significantly increase the performance of the highest-end computer chips.

Further, if you think about it, a "chip" is defined by its flatness. Semiconductors are 2D artifacts primarily because they are made under gravity. Connecting logic gates and circuits on these flat surfaces with the shortest path is a frustrating design challenge. Efforts are underway to make multilayered chips, but the interconnections on those are difficult. A truly three-dimensional semiconductor, in the form of a layered cube or even a sphere, that allowed for the shortest and simplest interconnections to all the gates could dramatically revolutionize computing. Researchers at universities and private companies are working with NASA on technologies to take semiconductors to the next level via in-space manufacturing.[121] Three-dimensional printing of semiconductors in space could give a needed extension to Moore's Law, the observation by Intel cofounder Gordon Moore, that the number of transistors on a chip will double every couple of years.

Compounds and crystals aren't the only materials that can be optimized in space. Metallic alloys can be more perfectly formed when lighter and heavier elements can be perfectly mixed. Not only that, but entirely new classes of materials like metallic glass and metal foams have been formed in the absence of gravity. The European Space Agency notes that experiments on the ISS show that "aluminum foam is as strong as pure metal but much lighter" and that microgravity research "can help in the construction of lightweight and sturdy aerospace structures and new shielding systems for diagnostic radiology equipment in hospitals."[122] It may also be possible to make high-temperature superconductors and more powerful magnets in space.[123] By removing the need for expensive and difficult-to-handle liquid helium cooling, high-temperature superconductor systems could revolutionize research into nuclear fusion and even medical imaging.

IT'S ALIVE! GROWING ORGANS IN SPACE

Living organisms function differently in space as well. This is a challenge for astronauts, as bone density, vision, and cognition can all be negatively affected by long-term exposure to microgravity. On the other hand, cell cultures actually grow exponentially faster in an environment where they can expand three-dimensionally, and oxygen and nutrients flow more easily. Cells grown in space also exhibit modified gene expression and other characteristics that have led researchers to believe significant progress can be made both in research and in development of biomedical products.

Consider organ replacement. Scientists can produce customized stem cells from your body and differentiate them into, for instance, liver cells. However, when they try to grow those cells into an actual liver on Earth, they get a liver pancake without the veins and arteries needed to support an organ. On the International Space Station, astronauts have taken the same cells and 3D-printed them into a three-dimensional structure with the vascularization required for an actual functioning "organoid."[124]

In 2023, NASA's In Space Production Applications (InSPA) program selected a proposal from the Wake Forest Institute for Regenerative Medicine to study 3D-printed liver tissue constructs on the ISS.[125] The goal is to grow custom livers, kidneys, hearts, cartilage, and other tissues in space and return them to Earth for implantation into patients requiring replacements. No more waiting for some poor organ donor to have a car accident or for the Chinese state to murder another Uighur or Falun Gong member for their global organ harvesting business.[126] These organs and tissues would be perfect DNA matches for the recipient, obviating the need for the costly and often dangerous course of immunosuppressant drugs that traditional organ recipients require for the rest of their lives.

In 2023, an experiment in 3D bioprinting conducted on the International Space Station by Redwire Corporation produced a human knee meniscus. Redwire executive vice president John Vellinger noted that "demonstrating the ability to successfully print complex tissue such as this meniscus is a major leap forward toward the development of a repeatable microgravity manufacturing process for reliable bioprinting at scale."[127] Additional types of tissues and organs are sure to follow.

Bringing sight to the blind is another promising area of space research. LambdaVision, of Farmington, Connecticut, has demonstrated the ability to produce an artificial retina on the ISS, where gravity does not interfere with the even distribution of light-activated proteins.[128] Their work is aimed at producing near-perfect two-hundred-layer thin films that should provide implants comparable to normal vision. Replacement retinas are anticipated to have a market price of $100,000 per unit (via insurance reimbursements). There are tens of thousands of Americans suffering from retinitis pigmentosa and even more with macular degeneration. Lambda-Vision is now testing the implants with animals and working with NASA's support to move the project towards commercial production.[129]

Microgravity also promises to revolutionize cancer research and treatments. The ability to grow and study 3D tumors could be transformative for researchers looking to understand how cancer cells organize and distribute themselves inside organs and the body.[130] Additionally, microgravity itself appears to suppress the growth of cancer cells, because the expression of certain genes associated with these cancers is reduced, and proteins involved in cancer cell reproduction are "down regulated." These effects have been demonstrated across multiple cancer cell lines including those of the lung, breast, colon, rectum, and thyroid.[131] A 2021 academic paper reviewing years of microgravity research concludes, "Based on these studies, we can conclude that microgravity affects cancer cells via inhibition of survival signaling pathways and induction of programmed cell death."[132]

THE EXTREME OPPOSITE OF "LOCALLY GROWN"

Growing human cells is not the only possible upside of space research. It may be possible to solve the problem of growing 3D animal muscle and fat in space to produce thick "cultured steaks" in space without slaughter. Aleph Farms, an Israeli company, has demonstrated this on the ISS.[133] Space meat may just be a treat for astronauts and future space colonists, or it may end up on an earthbound table near you, if the commercial space boom can drive the transportation costs low enough.

WHY "NOTHING" MAY BE OF GREAT VALUE

Space is airless—the reason why "no one can hear you scream"—and offers researchers and manufacturers access to a nearly perfect vacuum. Vacuum is something, or more correctly, nothing, that many specialized manufacturing processes demand, and producing a very high-quality vacuum in a large chamber is difficult and expensive on Earth. Even the brutal radiation environment of space can be utilized for some good. Experiments are underway to use this harsh environment to produce new materials and medical breakthroughs. We call this idea of producing materials and products in space In-Space Manufacturing (ISM).

An important externality of ISM is that it does not despoil Earth's precious water, air, or soil with factory pollutants. That said, all materials are precious in a realm where cargo transport is uncommonly expensive. Recycling everything possible is already the norm on the International Space Station, and accumulation of trash is discouraged. Taking out the trash involves packing this stuff into a non-reusable spacecraft (Northrop Grumman Cygnus or Russian Progress capsules), which are then intentionally injected into a reentry profile that burns the waste and vehicles up. Meanwhile, astro-rubbish must be stored, and although the station is the length of a football field and offers the volume of a 747, it is a busy, crowded place. Because of the value of raw materials and the disposal cost, space manufacturing is likely to incorporate the cleanest and most efficient production processes. Spin-offs from ISM technologies and practices are likely to reduce pollution, improve safety, and increase the productivity of earthbound factories as well.

Although we hold a real lead, space manufacturing will not be an American industry by default. Chinese academics and engineers are also excited by ISM. A book by Chinese researchers[134] shows that SJ-10, a satellite launched from Western China in 2016 and recovered in Inner Mongolia, conducted experiments on semiconductor crystal improvement,[135] material behaviors, the impact of radiation on DNA, and how animal embryos develop in space.[136] America can stay ahead of the competition by continuing to fund ISM research and by supporting the development and operation of commercial space stations, along with other free nations. NASA has been doing this for several years.[137] Houston's Johnson Space Center recently established the In Space Production Applications program to focus on this important area of economic development by supporting actual manufacturing tests for products with identifiable markets and effective business models.[138]

While the promise of making things in space for the benefit of us here on Earth is huge, it does require "downmass," or the capability to bring materials down from space. With most of the world's governmental and commercial space efforts focused on new rockets designed to put things up into space, there has been less focus on bringing things back to Earth. With the retirement of the Space Shuttle in 2012, we have only one proven and practical option for returning materials, SpaceX's Dragon 2 capsule. There are several commercial downmass systems under development, and we will discuss them and the challenges of downmass in chapter 6. Suffice to say that bringing things back to Earth is actually more challenging and expensive than lofting them to space.

MAKING IT FOR SPACE

One way to avoid the complexity and expense of bringing manufactured items down to Earth is to find a market for them in space. Products manufactured on-orbit or on the Moon would provide savings in time and dollars to customers already in space.

On the demand side, people living and working in space will be dependent on infrastructure and robotic systems. These systems will also require resupply and servicing. The parts and materials they need are readily available on Earth, but—as we discussed earlier with water—there is a very real cost in time and money to getting anything up and out of Earth's gravity well. So, we will likely have both a desire on the part of manufacturers to supply a space economy, and a demand from in-space customers for a lower-priced supply chain.

Companies are already looking at both the materials and finished goods they can supply to the space economy. Satellites and space stations require bulky structures to support things like cooling arrays, antennas, and solar panels. These items are often intricately folded, like an origami, inside of the fairing of a rocket, which is the cone at the top of a rocket that holds the payload. When the rocket's upper stage reaches space, the fairing opens up, and the payload is ejected. It must then carefully unfold and extend those arrays and antennas. This is a very common point of failure for many missions. Producing these structures in space would greatly reduce the design complexity, cost, and failure rate of space systems. Made in Space, a division of Redwire, developed a large, zero-gravity 3D printer, which can print out a continuous structural beam. They called this system Archinaut. Working with NASA and Northrop Grumman, the company was able to test the printer in thermal vacuum chambers that simulate space. In 2020, they successfully produced a seven-meter (twenty-three-foot) beam-like structure from their printer. NASA's Science Technology Mission Directorate provided funding for this under a program called "On-Orbit Servicing, Assembly, and Manufacturing 2" aka OSAM-2. Made in Space had scheduled to launch a test Archinaut satellite in 2024. The spacecraft would have printed a ten-meter beam from one side of the craft and a six-meter beam from the other. However, congressional budget pressures and a difficult investment environment appear to have resulted in the cancellation of the OSAM-2 project just before its completion.[139] Other firms are exploring this technology, and the DoD has shown interest in the capability.[140]

REAL SOLAR POWER

The most powerful resource in space is energy, specifically the massive amount of power blasting out from the incredible nuclear fusion plant that is our own Sun. Look at a picture of any modern satellite, Mars probe, or even the International Space Station. The most striking attributes are the large solar panels jutting from the core of the spacecraft.

In 1953, semiconductor scientists at Bell Labs were investigating the ability of some of their new materials to generate electricity when exposed to light. They got about 2 percent to 4 percent of the light hitting the cells converted into electrical current. Hoffman Electronics licensed the Bell patents and began producing small photovoltaic (PV) panels. Hoffman targeted the hobby and toy market but found very little interest. Disposable batteries were more powerful, readily available, and inexpensive. There was, however, an emerging domain where replacing batteries was not an option: space.[141]

Dr. Hans Ziegler, head of the US Signal Corps, was privy to America's secret plans to launch satellites and saw that they would be seriously limited by the weight and short life of their batteries. The Soviet Sputnik and American Explorer 1 both failed when their batteries died after a few weeks. Ziegler persuaded the Navy to put Hoffman panels on America's second satellite, Vanguard 1, which was launched in 1958. The elimination of batteries allowed Vanguard to be so small that it could be held in one hand. Soviet premier Nikita Khrushchev referred to America's little round satellite as "the grapefruit," fatefully mistaking its diminutive size as a weakness. Vanguard's compact design was really a powerful demonstration of American technical superiority. Vanguard continued transmitting for three years and remains the oldest human object in space. The grapefruit is still up there; the Soviet Union is just a bad memory.

Since then, nearly every satellite has been solar powered. We simply would not have any of the benefits (communications, imaging, GPS) listed in the previous chapter without solar power, and we would not have solar power in our homes or businesses if it were not for our investment in space. NASA, the DoD, and commercial space operators drove the leading-edge demand for lighter, more durable, and more efficient solar cells and panels, and these technologies eventually filtered down to terrestrial applications.[142]

Despite the hype of "renewable" and "sustainable" energy advocates, solar power on Earth has some serious limitations. Solar (and wind) are low-density energy sources. Despite efficiencies now approaching 40 percent in the lab and the mid-twenties in practice, it takes a whole lot of solar panels to generate enough electricity to run a modern city, and that's before you make all the cars electric. The installation of massive solar and wind farms seriously disrupts the environment, and to many they are a blight on the landscape. In Germany and other "progressive" countries, forests, along with their animal inhabitants, are being cleared to make way for huge tracks of sterile solar panels and windmills, all in the name of "environmentalism."

Additionally, wind and solar are unreliable as baseline power sources. Solar and wind depend on the weather, and therefore we can't depend on them. Solar is, of course, off all night long, just when people are charging those electric cars. It is also less than useful during the short, cloudy, and snowy days of high-latitude winters. On the best of days, in the best of environments—say on a parking cover in Phoenix, during the summer—solar panels only generate significant power for ten or twelve hours out of twenty-four. In most places, the window is more like five to eight hours. Despite the constant green hyperbole, there is currently no reasonable storage solution for the sort of power required to run an industrial civilization while solar and wind take breaks. In a TED talk advocating for nuclear power, Bill Gates noted that using all the batteries on Earth to store renewable power would work only for a few minutes.[143] Building enough batteries to run our civilization for a single night would require so much strip-mining and metal processing that it might wreck our planet. Once again, space offers us a possible solution.

Solar panels can be positioned in Earth orbit so they have continuous exposure to the Sun 24-7, 365. In space, there is no night, no clouds, and no atmosphere to filter out a lot of the solar energy. In many years of space applications, solar panels have been shown to generate significantly more energy than comparable ground installations. Estimates range up to thirteen times more efficient than similar ground-based installations.[144] What if you could run a cable down to Earth and bring all that cheap, clean power to a city?

It shouldn't be surprising that we will not be running an extension cord to a big power socket in space, but did you know it is possible to beam energy from one place to another? That is essentially what broadcast radio and TV are—electrical signals transmitted over a distance. The early electrical innovator Nikola Tesla obtained funding from J. P. Morgan to work on the transmission of electricity at a remote facility he built in Colorado Springs.[145] Today, wireless power transmission using microwaves and lasers has been demonstrated over distances of many miles.[146] Beaming power from a satellite, in a geosynchronous orbit, to a ground rectifier (antenna) is entirely practical. It is likely that about half the power would lost be in the transmission and conversion, but since the initial generating efficiency is so much higher and always on, that is a small price to pay. A visionary engineer from NASA's Apollo program, Peter Glaser, patented this concept in 1973.[147]

John Mankins, of the National Space Society, is a champion of space-based solar power (SBSP, SPS). In his book *The Case for Space Solar Power*, Mankins produces a detailed design for a five-gigawatt solar satellite that supplies two gigawatts to any point on the continent it hovers above. The receiver could be an array of wires underground, perhaps a kilometer square or so. While it would likely be located out of town, the frequency of the beam and its energy density would be safe for planes, birds, or other animals to pass through without notice. Such systems promise robust economic growth without significant land utilization or pollution of any kind. While that is a big, probably billion-dollar project, smaller versions of his SPS-ALPHA could be deployed soon and provide power to selected niche markets in remote locations. These might include disaster relief efforts, providing power to hospitals and emergency responders in powerless areas following hurricanes or earthquakes.[148]

It would also be possible to beam power with an optical laser to a normal solar panel. Although it might be less efficient (the panels are only about 25 percent efficient to begin with), this option offers remarkable flexibility to deliver power to existing systems on Earth in an emergency or perhaps even power other satellites in space or landers on the Moon.[149] Other strategies involve using a microwave beam or laser to heat water or other liquids to drive turbines.

Understanding the potential of space solar power, you won't be surprised to hear that China plans to dominate the field. China has been talking about becoming "the first country to build a space solar power station with practical value" for several years.[150] The China Academy of Space Technology (CAST) announced the launch of a "space high voltage transfer and wireless power transmission experiment" to low Earth orbit in 2028 and an operational megawatt facility in geosynchronous orbit by 2030.[151] Mankins commented, "There is absolutely progress from the Chinese at this point. This is not posturing; this is a real plan from serious organizations with revered scientists in China. They have a perfectly good technical plan, and they can do it by 2030."[152] Details of the technology were published in a Chinese academic journal in 2022.[153]

John Mankins was pleased with the Chinese commitment and hopes it will spark a possible renewal of US interest in the project. "The dramatically stated interest on the part of the Chinese will do a lot to engender interest."[154] While that is true, and we'd all like to see the world's biggest polluter cut their emissions, there may be a dark side to China's interest in beaming power to Earth.

Mankins's space power station is designed to be safe for people and living things. Choosing a microwave frequency that does not interact with the molecules in our bodies and keeping the beam footprint on the ground fairly wide ensures this. On the other hand, anyone who has stuck a beverage into their microwave oven knows that these beams are capable of imparting significant energy into material. Your "radar range" (as they used to be called) is set to a frequency (2.4 gigahertz) that is effective at inducing charges in water and fat molecules, which causes them to move.[iii] If the solar power station beam was tunable to that frequency (or many others)

---

iii   This is also the primary frequency for Wi-Fi and many consumers' remote control products.

and focusable on a smaller target, it could become that James Bond death ray. Multigigawatt lasers could obviously be used for weapons systems as well.

One might imagine a scenario where China would "provide" power to its client states in South America and Africa by parking such an SSP station on the equator over those continents. A quick retuning, refocusing, and retargeting of the beam northward could threaten people or facilities in military and civilian installations across North America or Europe.

It has also been suggested that an adjustable beam could be used to make people very uncomfortable as a tool for dealing with urban insurgents or to provide riot or crowd control from above. As noted in chapter 10, China has been developing directed energy weapons for use against satellites, and they have them for use on Earth as well. Evidence suggests that they may have been used against US diplomats.[155] China may have used the tool against Indian troops in a border region of the Indian Himalayas that China has been trying to occupy.[156] *The Times of London* reported that a Chinese professor of international relations publicly bragged of China's People's Liberation Army's "beautiful" countering of Indian advances in Ladakh with an energy weapon that "turned the mountain tops into a microwave oven."[157]

The US military has a system called the Active Denial System (ADS) that uses a nonlethal ninety-five-gigahertz directed energy beam. This system is designed to heat the skin of opponents to an uncomfortable temperature at a distance that goes beyond the range of small arms. ADS has been tested on human volunteers and is rated "suitable for operational employment," though there is no suggestion that it has been used in combat.[158]

Aside from the caution we must show with dual-use technologies, the bottom line is that extracting resources from space, processing them in space, and producing products and energy in space would deliver an economic boom for America and benefit the entire planet. Doing this off-world allows for economic growth while sidestepping the Malthusian traps of resource limits and the negative externalities of pollution. It's a brighter future, and it should be no wonder that the no-growth crowd, who prefer a future where circumstances allow them to insist that ambitions be restrained and that individuals must be controlled by governments, have stepped up their opposition to space development and settlement. Globe-trotting, multimillionaire climate activist Greta Thunberg recently produced a video mocking plans to colonize Mars and publicly urged Elon Musk to "stay grounded rather than to travel in space, because there are more important things to focus on right now, more important resources that we should invest money in."[159]

If America takes Greta's bad advice and fails to develop space, we will surely be yielding the ultimate high ground to a rapacious and unscrupulous China. The results of this blunder would mirror the disastrous isolationism of China's Ming dynasty and define the nature of human civilization for centuries. Luckily, Musk has not been listening to such misguided admonitions.

LESSONS LEARNED: COMMERCIAL SPACE WILL TRANSFORM OUR FUTURE

We must develop space. American policies and regulations must encourage, facilitate, and promote the extraction of space resources.

NASA must work with traditional and New Space firms to secure prime resource locations on the Moon's surface before China does.

Supporting fundamental research and encouraging private investment in in-space manufacturing will be critical in recapturing our position as the "workshop to the world," the one sure path to prosperity and power.

Developing space solar power technology ahead of China is critical. Keeping Chinese space-based solar power platforms out of our hemisphere is a national security necessity.

CHAPTER SIX

FINDING THE FUTURE: FROM FRITZ LANG TO SATELLITES

*Every vision is a joke until the
first man accomplishes it.*
—Robert Goddard

H umanity stands at a monumental historical tipping point. Economically, it is as significant as the dramatic global changes that occurred during the Age of Exploration of the fifteenth, sixteenth, and seventeenth centuries. Socially, it is as important as the "Out of Africa" movement, when modern humans migrated from what is now Ethiopia some seventy thousand to three hundred thousand[i] years ago. Biologically, it may be as important as the Devonian fishes that crawled from a shallow sea to survive on land some three hundred to four hundred million years ago.

---

i   While there is broad agreement that we all descended from the first modern humans in East Africa, there is debate about the timing of the migration, which probably took place in many waves.

It is likely that some people living today will leave the cradle of our home planet, never to return. They will settle on the Moon, Mars, and orbiting space stations. They will extend our planet's fragile biosphere and make Homo sapiens a multiplanetary species. We have the technology to accomplish this and both commercial and governmental organizations ready to go. "Occupy Mars" is the cry of Elon Musk's SpaceX.[160] Jeff Bezos wants to see "millions of people living and working in space."[161] President Trump amended US space policy[ii] to specifically call for "an innovative and sustainable program of exploration with commercial and international partners to *enable human expansion across the solar system*."[162]

It feels as if we have suddenly arrived in the future, and yet there are a hundred years of bold thinking, daring acts, and tragic mistakes that should inform the wisdom of good policymakers and successful business leaders. As Edmund Burke advised, "People will not look forward to posterity, who never look backward to their ancestors." Let us now consider how we reached the Space Age.

SPACEFLIGHT HAS THREE FATHERS

In October of 1929, a remarkable new movie opened in Berlin. *Frau im Mond* (*Woman in the Moon*) was based on the novel *The Rocket to the Moon* by Thea von Harbou, the wife of the film's visionary director, Fritz Lang. The film featured a daring space entrepreneur seeking to mine gold on the Moon while battling against a cabal of evil corporate competitors. *Frau im Mond* marked the pinnacle of the "German rocket craze," a social

---

ii   In a rare area of policy continuity, the Biden White House and NASA team have broadly retained and built upon Trump space policy.

phenomenon that swept a country following their loss in the First World War. Germany was a nation desperately seeking purpose under the punishing and humiliating terms of the Treaty of Versailles. Germans of all ages and from all walks of life joined dreamy rocket clubs and quirky startups dedicated to exploring and exploiting space.[163]

Harbou's novel and the rocket craze were inspired by a 1923 science text, *Die Rakete zu den Planetenräumen* (*The Rocket into Interplanetary Space*) by Hermann Oberth.[164] In it, the Transylvanian physicist described important techniques that would make space travel possible, including the multi-stage rocket. Oberth served as technical advisor for Lang's film, which was so accurate that it still draws kudos for its "realism." *Frau im Mond* featured many of NASA's modern launch elements, including a huge vertical integration building, a crawler to transport the rocket to the pad, and the recumbent seats astronauts would use to absorb g-forces during launch. It also introduced the "countdown," a device Lang invented to create tension in his film.[165] During the craze, Oberth assisted rocket clubs and mentored real rocket builders, including a young Wernher von Braun.

Science fiction has always been integral to the work of actual space pioneers. Oberth's space science was inspired by his repeated readings of Jules Verne's novels *From the Earth to the Moon* and *Around the Moon*. Verne's nineteenth-century vision was eerily prescient. The French author described mankind's first flight to the Moon as an American project, shot from a massive cannon in Florida, roughly a hundred miles from the actual Apollo launch pad at Cape Canaveral. Verne's spacecraft, *Columbiad*, circled the Moon and then splashed down in the Pacific Ocean, where it was retrieved by a US Navy ship, as was the actual Apollo 11 capsule, *Columbia*.

Meanwhile, across the Atlantic, a more practical American was thinking along similar lines as Oberth and flying his own hardware. Growing up in New England, Robert Goddard was inspired by the writings of H. G. Wells and the possibility of interplanetary travel in *The War of the Worlds*. Seated high in a cherry tree on his family's farm, a seventeen-year-old Goddard pondered Wells and experienced an epiphany that would change his life and the world. He imagined that he could build a vehicle capable of reaching Mars, and he would never let go of that vision. He later remarked, "I was a different boy when I descended the tree from when I ascended. Existence at last seemed very purposive." The date was October 19, 1899, and Goddard would always refer to it as his "Anniversary Day."[166]

Before Goddard, all rockets were powered by tightly packed gunpowder, a design dating back to medieval China. Goddard had also independently developed the critical concept of multistage launch vehicles and placed the first non-destructive payloads onto a rocket when he launched a camera and a barometer in 1929.[167] However, the visionary professor always struggled for cash to fund his obscure work. His letters found some support with the Secretary of the Smithsonian, Charles Greeley Abbot, who provided $5,000. Goddard's mother enthused over this, "Think of it! You send the Government some typewritten sheets and some pictures, and they send you $1,000, and tell you they are going to send four more." The famous aviator Charles Lindbergh managed to pry $50,000 out of the Guggenheim Foundation to support Goddard's work.[168] In total, Goddard appears to have spent less than $200,000 during his career as America's leading rocket scientist. As we will see, things were very different across the Atlantic.

While he dreamed of sending humans to the moon, Professor Goddard quickly learned that disruptive visionaries are rarely welcomed. Despite a successful academic career culminating in a professorship at Clark College, his vision was often the victim of mean-spirited and ignorant criticism from the mainstream media of his day. After one of Goddard's successful test flights, a Worcester paper ran the headline, "Moon Rocket Misses Target by 238,799½ Miles."[169]

On January 13, 1920, *The New York Times* published an article entitled, "A Severe Strain on Credulity," a blistering editorial attacking Goddard's grant from the Smithsonian. The *Times* editors mockingly asserted that rockets could not work in space because:

> Professor Goddard, with his 'chair' in Clark College and the countenancing of the Smithsonian Institution, does not know the relation of action to reaction, and of the need to have something better than a vacuum against which to react. He only seems to lack the knowledge ladled out daily in high schools.[iii]

The third member of the early twentieth-century rocket triumvirate was Konstantin Eduardovich Tsiolkovsky, a Polish-Russian scientist who did early work on aviation and designed metal-skinned dirigibles and aircraft decades before they were deployed. Also a fan of Jules Verne's Moon novels, Tsiolkovsky began to find a safer way to transport humans into space than Verne's big cannon.[170] In 1897, he perfected the mathematical equation that defines the performance of

---

iii   On July 17, 1969, the day after Apollo 11 launched to the Moon, the *Times* published a droll retraction of their 1920 statement.

a rocket launch. This famous "rocket equation" models the relationship between the initial mass of the rocket, the thrust it generates via the speed of its exhaust, and the velocity it can attain. The equation made it clear that multistage rockets would be required to escape Earth's gravity and reach the Moon. In 1903, he published "Exploration of Outer Space by Means of Rocket Devices" (Исследование мировых пространств реактивными приборами), which detailed in great precision the technologies required to reach orbit and accurately calculated the orbital speed of 18,000 mph for a satellite in LEO.[171] Tsiolkovsky proposed the use of liquid hydrogen fuel with liquid oxygen as an oxidizer, the same propellants used by NASA's Space Launch System (SLS) rocket, which will soon return American astronauts to the Moon.[iv]

In 1930, a group of science fiction writers "dreaming about spaceflight" founded the American Interplanetary Society. Reorganized in 1963 as the American Institute of Aeronautics and Astronautics, the AIAA is now the premier professional organization for aerospace engineers, with almost thirty thousand members across the globe. AIAA hosts some of the most important conferences.[172]

EARTH'S FIRST SPACE ROCKET LANDS ON THE WRONG PLANET

While Robert Goddard struggled to build American rockets with a few thousand dollars, Oberth's protégé, Wernher von Braun, secured half a billion dollars in Nazi funding for his efforts to copy and improve upon the American scientist's designs for liquid rockets.[173] The investment paid off. On Oc-

---

iv   The Artemis 2 mission, in which four US astronauts will orbit the Moon, is currently scheduled for late 2025.

tober 3, 1942, one of von Braun's Aggregat 4 (A-4) rockets, powered by alcohol and liquid oxygen, was launched from the Army Research Center at Peenemünde, Germany. It climbed into the sky and exceeded fifty miles, the US governmental definition of space. On June 20, 1944, another V-2 test reached an altitude of 176 kilometers exceeding the "Kármán line" of 100 km commonly cited by many other nations as the border of space.

While von Braun was interested in the engineering of rockets for their own sake and to someday send humans to the Moon, his Nazi backers were looking for a weapon of terror to break the resolve of Winston Churchill and the British people. Hitler renamed the A-4 "V-2" for "Vengeance Weapon 2."[v] Rather than carrying a German astronaut to space, each rocket was used to deliver a ton of explosives into Allied cities. The German Wehrmacht built over three thousand V-2s, which killed nine thousand civilians in London and Antwerp in 1944 and 1945. This figure does not include the fate of enslaved workers from the Mittelbau-Dora concentration camp who were forced to build rockets under inhuman conditions, often deep underground. Deflecting criticism over all this, von Braun is often said to have epigrammatically remarked that "the rocket worked perfectly but landed on the wrong planet."[174]

Near the end of the war, Robert Goddard was able to inspect components from the V-2 rockets that pummeled England. The underfunded American would recognize his work on gyroscopic guidance, gimbals, and fuel pumps.[175] That

v   Vengeance Weapon 1, the V-1, was an autonomous jet plane—the world's first cruise missile—known to the British as the "buzz bomb" because of the unusual noise it produced.

image should serve as a cautionary tale for today's congressional budget cutters in the face of rapidly escalating Chinese investments in copying and improving on American rocket and space technologies.

While the V-2 thankfully arrived too late to save Hitler, it did change the face of warfare forever. The Germans also built and deployed rocket-powered planes and had designs for a suborbital spaceplane called "Silver Bird," which was specifically designed to drop bombs (possibly atomic) on New York City.[176]

PROJECT PAPERCLIP

Understanding the power and the threat posed by advanced Nazi technologies, US military intelligence launched Project Paperclip in 1945. Agents were charged with locating and retrieving top German scientists, particularly those working on rockets, before they fell into the hands of Soviet forces occupying much of Eastern Germany.

Fearing life in Stalin's Soviet Union, von Braun and his team were more than cooperative. They hid a huge cache of V-2 technology and documents in caves and marched over mountains in order to find Americans they could surrender to. Von Braun had broken his arm during the march. He was patched up and shipped off to Fort Bliss, Texas, along with the hoard of German rocket parts.

BOMBING MEXICO

Living in El Paso, the Germans ran their own shop assembling V-2s from German parts and launched German rockets from New Mexico's White Sands Missile Range. Working with Americans and integrating US hardware, they began to enhance the V-2, achieve higher altitudes, and replace the destructive payloads with scientific and engineering experiments. In October of 1946, a modified US V-2 took the first photos from space.[177] On June 14, 1949, Albert II, a rhesus monkey, became the first Earthling to travel into space! [178,vi] This was eight years before the Soviets sent a dog, Laika, into orbit.

One V-2 test flight was particularly memorable and nearly sparked an international incident. On May 29, 1947, von Braun's team launched a highly modified new two-stage rocket topped with a mock-up cruise missile. The V-2 veered off course and headed south toward El Paso. One of the Germans, Ernst Steinhoff, reported that he was the actual range safety officer (RSO) responsible for ordering the destruction of wayward rockets. He knew that crashing a V-2 filled with alcohol and liquid oxygen into one of these cities might have resulted in mass casualties. Steinhoff did a quick calculation and decided it was best to let the rocket overfly El Paso and the Mexican city of Juarez and hope it expended all its propellants before it crashed. He ordered the sailor at "the button" to stand down. During the incident investigation that followed, a US Army officer said, admiringly, of the German, "I've never seen such a cold-blooded bastard."[179]

The rocket crashed to the ground near a cemetery south of Juarez. The explosive impact shook windows on both sides of the border and left a massive crater. Nobody was injured, and collectors scavenged the remains of the vehicle.[180] Steinhoff

---

vi   Sadly, the V-2 lacked any reentry or recovery system, and Albert did not survive his flight. Future US-designed rockets did safely recover their animal astronauts.

reported that local vendors began to sell V-2 parts to local visitors, sometimes substituting whatever metal scrap they could find when the crater ran dry.[181] No international incident was forthcoming, and tourists still visit the crater today.

TO THE MOON VIA THE EL PASO ROTARY CLUB

The Germans at Fort Bliss showed no hesitation in once again being directed to develop weapons systems, this time for the US military. Beyond being extremely transactional, they despised the Soviets nearly much as they had loved Germany. However, von Braun's real objective remained the science fiction dream of humans in space and of sending men to the Moon. The rocket scientist was smart enough to know that he would never convince the US Army to fund a science mission to the Moon. Understanding America was a democracy, he developed the surprising plan of speaking directly to the American people about their future in space.

In the late 1940s, America was a "down-to-earth" nation of middle-class workers still licking the wounds of a war inflicted upon them by von Braun's countrymen. Almost everyone knew someone who had been killed or maimed in the conflict. They had all sacrificed for years to fund and support the war effort. Imagine a heavily accented Teutonic aristocrat, with little natural empathy and a Nazi past,[vii] setting out to sell space travel to those folks.

It is hard to imagine a less appropriate venue for the first speech on national space policy than the Rotary Club of El

---

vii Though he was fairly non-political, von Braun had joined the Nazi Party and was even recruited—he said under threat and only to get his rockets built—into Hitler's elite SS paramilitary corps.

Paso, Texas. However, in early 1947, von Braun walked into that humble building and shared his passion for space with a group of dusty cowboys, shop owners, and local politicians. He explained the mechanics of rockets and how satellites would work. He argued for America building a human space station, a Space Shuttle, and eventually sending people to the Moon and Mars.[182]

This speech was just the start of von Braun's quixotic journey into public influence. He would speak to anyone who would listen about space. He spoke to the NATO generals and to the Mississippi Dental Association.[183] He wrote a science fiction novel in German. The book entitled *Marsprojekt* was translated into English as *The Mars Project* by a US naval officer. It was cleared for publication by the DoD as "too futuristic to infringe on classified matters" and released in magazine serializations starting during the 1950s. It detailed the technology of spaceflight and explored the ethics of technology through meetings with the alien inhabitants of the Red Planet, whose leader was ironically addressed as, "The Elon."[184]

Von Braun's compelling articles eventually excited the passion of America's greatest visionary and storyteller. Walt Disney was building the amusement park of his dreams in Anaheim, California, and preparing a television series to promote it that would also be called "Disneyland."[viii] Von Braun served as a technical consultant on both projects and made several appearances on the TV show starting with an episode entitled "Man and the Moon" in December of 1955.[185] Von Braun's plan had triumphed. Space caught fire in 1950s America, much as it had in 1920s Germany. Sci-fi space films

---

viii The popular series was later known as "Walt Disney's Wonderful World of Color" and "The Wonderful World of Disney."

proliferated. Toys, kitchen appliances, and automobiles began to take on a rocket-inspired design aesthetic.

THE STUPIDEST THING THIS COUNTRY EVER DID

Everything was not perfect, however. Post war tensions between the US and the Soviets had rapidly escalated. In 1946, Churchill warned that an "Iron Curtain" was descending on Eastern Europe. In 1949, Mao's communist forces overran the Nationalist Chinese Republic with Soviet help. In that same year, the Soviets demonstrated an atomic bomb, shocking and terrifying America. Worse, American and British collaborators were found to have handed secret weapons technology, including atomic bomb designs, to the Russians.[186] The following year, Moscow's puppet regime in North Korea invaded the south with Mao's support, and Americans were once again fighting and dying in an overseas war.

Caught like a fly in the middle of this web of international intrigue and domestic suspicion was one of the most significant, yet rarely mentioned, figures of the twentieth century. Growing up in China during the pre-communist Republic, Qian Xuesen[ix] was admitted to MIT in 1935 on a Boxer Indemnity Scholarship[x] and earned an MS in aeronautical en-

---

ix　錢學森,alternative Latinized alphabet spelling: Hsue-Shen Tsien.

x　In 1899, a group of Chinese youths known as the "Boxers" rebelled against Western powers that had been commercially and militarily subjugating China during what was known as the "century of humiliation." When the Boxers burned merchant warehouses and factories, a joint force of European and American forces put down the rebellion and demanded reparations from the Chinese. US president Teddy Roosevelt felt the money was ill-gotten and used the funds to educate the youth of gineering. He then traveled to Caltech to earn a PhD under the illustrious Theodore von Kármán, whose group included future movers and shakers of space technology like Jack Parsons and Frank Malina. At Caltech, von Kármán enthused of Qian, "He was an undisputed genius whose work was providing an enormous impetus to advances in high-speed aerodynamics and jet propulsion."[187] This group began flying their self-built rockets in a remote arroyo outside of Pasadena at a site that now houses Caltech's Jet Propulsion Laboratory (JPL). JPL, which Qian cofounded, designs and operates the majority of NASA's deep space exploration probes and rovers. Among the innovations that Qian fostered while working at Caltech was the concept of suborbital point-to-point (P2P) space transportation and a winged spaceplane. This idea inspired the USAF project Dyna-Soar that influenced the design of the Space Shuttle.

Qian Xuesen eventually became the Robert H. Goddard professor of jet propulsion at Caltech, one of the most prestigious positions a professor of aerospace engineering could obtain. At the end of the Second World War, Qian was given an appointment as a colonel in the United States Army and was sent to Germany to assist in the effort to identify top German rocket scientists. This was remarkable, given the segregated nature of the military at the time and the fact that the Chinese scientist was not an American citizen.

As the Cold War heated up, the Red Scare swept up the guilty, the innocent, and the ambiguous. When Qian applied for citizenship in 1949, a background check revealed that he had attended a communist party meeting in a Pasadena

China. The money helped found Beijing's prestigious Tsinghua University and brought Qian Xuesen and many other Chinese students to American universities.

apartment many years earlier. These gatherings had been an unfortunately fashionable trend in the '30s. Many of America's top nuclear and rocket scientists, including Frank Malina and Robert Oppenheimer, had also participated in them. It is unlikely that Qian was actually a communist sympathizer. His wife was even the daughter of one of the top lieutenants of Chiang Kai-shek's Nationalist Chinese government who fled to Taiwan following the communist takeover of the mainland. In June of 1950, Qian was briefly imprisoned on Terminal Island in San Pedro Harbor. He was released to house arrest and stripped of his security clearances. This effectively ended his career as one of America's top military rocket designers.

In 1955, the Eisenhower administration agreed to trade Qian to China in exchange for five US pilots that had been captured by the Chinese. Regardless of Qian's guilt or innocence, sending one of America's top rocket designers to China was an absolutely boneheaded piece of statecraft. Nothing could be more emblematic of America's anti-strategic approach to Communist China. If we've gotten you worried about the Chinese space threat America now faces, you can blame the FBI for starting what Navy under secretary Dan Kimball called the "stupidest thing this country ever did."[188] Once in China, a deeply embittered Qian quickly embraced Mao and jump-started China's rocket development efforts. He is considered to be the father of both their ICBM and space exploration programs.[189] Many of Qian's Caltech colleagues continued to vouch for him until his death in 2009.[190]

THE CHIEF DESIGNER

Von Braun and Qian had a counterpart in Russia. Sergei Pavlovich Korolev, the father of the Soviet space program, was born on January 12, 1907, in what is now Ukraine. During his career, Korolev worked without a name and could only be publicly referred to as "Chief Designer" (Главный Конструктор). This anonymity was instituted by the KGB to safeguard this important Soviet asset from elicitation or assassination by Western spies. Ironically, and typical in communist regimes, Korolev had spent several years as a political prisoner in the Soviet gulag (1938–1944) after being accused of "counter-revolutionary activities," before being rehabilitated in 1944 and eventually declared a "Hero of Labor."[191] During the heyday of Soviet space accomplishment, the Chief Designer could do no wrong. Cosmonaut Alexei Leonov recalled:

> For those on the space program there was no authority higher. Korolev had the reputation of being a man of the highest integrity, but also of being extremely demanding. Everyone around him was on tenterhooks, afraid of making a wrong move and invoking his wrath. He was treated like a god.

The Chief Designer had been inspired as a young child by a visit to an air show in 1913 and began to study flight on his own. He began to build and fly gliders and was eventually admitted to the Bauman Moscow State Technical University where he was mentored by the famous Russian aircraft engineer Andrei Tupolev.[192]

In 1945, Korolev, much like Qian, was commissioned as a colonel in the Red Army and shipped to Germany as part of Operation Osoaviakhim, the Soviet version of Paperclip.[193] He worked with a member of von Braun's former team, Helmut

Gröttrup, and other German scientists to recover V-2 designs and components. Gröttrup and two thousand Germans were shipped to the Soviet Union to continue the work.[194]

Stalin ordered the development and production of a Russian duplicate of the German V-2 dubbed the "R-1."[195] Although the R-1 was of little use to the USSR, which needed a much longer-range weapon, it was an important first step in learning how to build rockets. The R-1 survives today as the Scud tactical missile.[xi] Some of these R-1s were later sent to jump-start Qian's missile program in China.[196]

Korolev eventually received permission to develop a series of domestic rockets starting with the R-2, which doubled the range of the R-1/V-2. In 1953, Korolev began work on the first intercontinental ballistic missile, the R-7. The R-7 was a massive two-stage rocket with four large strap-on boosters and twenty kerosene-burning engines. It had to be immensely powerful, because the Soviets' comparatively primitive nuclear weapons were far larger and much more massive than their American counterparts. This lack of technical sophistication drove the Russians to build bigger rockets, giving them a leg up in the space race when it arrived. A modified R-7 would launch Sputnik into orbit in 1957, and variants of this design would get cosmonauts into space.

RACING HARD FOR SECOND PLACE

As the International Geophysical Year (1957) approached, and the race with the Soviets was on to launch an artificial satellite, von Braun's group had been relocated from Texas to the Army's Redstone Arsenal in Huntsville, Alabama. The

xi   Twenty-eight American soldiers were killed by a Scud that hit their barracks during the First Gulf War.

Germans had built an improved version of the V-2, which they named "Redstone," after their new home. The two-stage Jupiter-Redstone rocket was both a ballistic missile and a potential space launch vehicle. Von Braun assumed his team would be given the go-ahead to launch America's first payload into space and began to work with scientist James van Allen to ensure that his satellite, Explorer 1, would fit the rocket's payload fairing. Despite the fact that the Redstone had made many successful flights and was based on proven V-2 heritage, the Eisenhower administration inexplicably awarded the first space launch to an inexperienced team from the Navy and ordered work stopped on the space variant of the Redstone.

Korolev's team launched Sputnik on October 4, 1957, shocking America and supporting a growing global perception that the Soviet Union's rise was unstoppable. The event prompted renowned British science fiction author, Arthur C. Clarke, to call the United States a "second-rate power." Meanwhile, the Navy's Vanguard program was fraught with problems and delays. This gave the Soviets time to launch a larger Sputnik 2, which carried an unfortunate dog, Laika, into space.[xii]

When launch day arrived on December 6, 1957, Vanguard 1 rose a few feet, then stalled and crashed back down on its own pad. The fully fueled rocket produced a massive fireball viewed by millions of humiliated Americans on TV. The press brutally mocked the Navy rocket as "Flopnik" and "Kaputnik."

At this point, the White House was forced to concede, and von Braun now had his chance. The Germans executed with

---

xii   Although Laika was regarded as a hero of the Soviet Union and adorned postage stamps, the ugly truth was that the Soviets had made no provision for her return. She died a miserable death from overheating before the scientists could euthanize her.

astounding speed. Von Braun's team was ready to go, and on the night of January 31, 1958, the Jupiter-Redstone launched van Allen's Explorer I into orbit. The American satellite was the first with an actual scientific purpose, and it mapped the radiation patterns around Earth that we now call the Van Allen belts.

The Eisenhower White House decision to favor the ill-prepared Vanguard program over the Redstone effort has puzzled space policy analysts for years. Though there is virtually no direct evidence to support the assertion, an interesting conspiracy theory maintains credibility among space insiders to this day.[197] The theory asserts that Eisenhower intentionally allowed the Soviets to beat the Americans into orbit in a move that mirrors the idea that FDR ignored intelligence indicating a Japanese attack on Pearl Harbor in order to get America fully into WWII. The idea is that Eisenhower knew the press and public would "freak out" with Soviet hardware flying over their heads. Meanwhile, American U-2 spy plane overflights of the Soviet Union were a clear violation of that country's airspace and subject to being shot down. However, no precedent or international law addressed the issue of crossing *above* a nation's airspace in orbit. If America launched the first satellite, the Soviet Union would surely object to it flying over their country, because they basically objected to everything. On the other hand, if Eisenhower allowed the Soviets to launch first and the US failed to object to the overflight, the USSR could hardly object to America doing the same. Then America could utilize its superior engineering and electronics capabilities to build satellites capable of taking high-quality photographs and intercepting communications across Russia. These were technologies in which the Soviets would always lag behind. The US did quickly obtain a spy satellite advantage and maintained it for decades.

Still, round one of the space race had clearly gone to the Soviets. As if to rub that in, they sent three probes to the Moon in 1958 and 1959, one of which became the first man-made object to leave Earth forever, one the first to impact on another celestial body, and one that returned the first photos of the far side of the Moon.

LESSONS LEARNED: PLAYING IN THE SPACE RACE IS NOT ENOUGH; WINNING IS REQUIRED

Other countries may have good ideas. In all the world, America has the unique power to absorb those ideas and their creators to increase our strength.

America needlessly legitimized Soviet technology and thereby the Soviet system by allowing them to orbit first and by our own early technological failures. This blunder was primarily driven by political decisions to protect insiders over outsiders within our own system.

We are in a similar race with China at the moment. The CCP is using every tool at hand to demonstrate the superiority of their neofascist political model and state-capitalist economic system. We cannot afford another "Sputnik moment." We must succeed as a space-faring nation. We must play every player on our team, including all our governmental agencies, our global allies, aerospace giants, and entrepreneurial startups, to maximum advantage.

CHAPTER FIVE

FOR ALL MANKIND: FROM YURI'S NIGHT TO THE MOON

*We choose to go to the Moon. We choose to go to
the Moon... We choose to go to the Moon in this
decade and do the other things, not because they
are easy, but because they are hard; because that
goal will serve to organize and measure the best of
our energies and skills, because that challenge is one
that we are willing to accept, one we are unwilling to
postpone, and one we intend to win.*
—John Fitzgerald Kennedy, Rice University 1962[i]

With space launch and satellites a reality, the next space objective had been clearly laid out by science fiction: put humans into space. Once again, the Soviets and Americans lined up to race to space, and once again, America ran for the silver.

---

i   If you've never heard JFK's Rice Moon speech, arguably one
     of the finest efforts in American political rhetoric, watch it at:
     https://youtu.be/iQV9CAJWlVY.

At 6:07 AM on April 12, 1961, Soviet pilot Yuri Gagarin was launched into space from the Baikonur Cosmodrome in Kazakhstan. As his Vostok 1 vehicle left the pad, the young cosmonaut radioed Korolev, "Поехали" or, "Off we go!" One hundred and eight minutes later and after just a single orbit, Gagarin reentered Earth's atmosphere, ejected from the capsule at seven thousand meters, and parachuted to Earth, becoming the first human being to leave our home planet. He had been promoted to major during his flight and was soon acclaimed as a "hero of the Soviet Union." Handsome, professional, and universally respected, Gagarin's accomplishment is still celebrated—mostly by Americans—at "Yuri's Night" parties every April.[198]

As detailed in Tom Wolfe's seminal novel, *The Right Stuff*,[199] America's Mercury 7 astronauts, including Alan Shepard, seethed with jealousy over Gagarin's success and boiled over with frustration at NASA's cautious pacing. America had successfully launched Ham the "astrochimp" on a suborbital spaceflight aboard a specialized Mercury spacecraft atop a Redstone-2 rocket on January 31.[200] Ham returned to splashdown and was safely recovered more than two months before Gagarin's flight. Alan Shepard essentially duplicated Ham's achievement with a fifteen-minute spaceflight on May 5, and Gus Grissom followed in July. Many felt that there was no practical reason why America had not claimed the title of "first man in space" rather than that of "first chimp in space." Even after a second Russian orbital mission succeeded in August of '61, NASA timidly delayed orbiting an American astronaut until they could run an orbital test with another astrochimp, Enos.[201] America finally orbited Friendship 7 with astronaut John Glenn on February 20, 1962. On June 16,

1963, the Russians launched a female cosmonaut, Valentina Tereshkova (Валентина Терешкова), an accomplishment that America would not duplicate for two more decades.

MEANWHILE, BACK AT THE RANCH

Up in California's dusty High Desert, there was a second American space program that received less attention than the big rocket launches out in Florida. Test pilots at Edwards Air Force Base were earning their astronaut wings flying the X-15. The X-15 was a rocket-powered plane launched from under a B-52 bomber, and it could fly outside Earth's atmosphere on suborbital missions and return to land on a runway or the big dry lake bed at Edwards.[202] Before he joined the Gemini program at NASA, Neil Armstrong was a civilian test pilot flying the X-15 at Edwards. Plans were made to extend the X-15 into an orbital spacecraft, but the program was cancelled in favor of NASA's Project Mercury.[203]

The next goals in human spaceflight were to launch a multicrew flight and conduct an extravehicular activity (EVA) aka "spacewalk." The Soviets launched a Voskhod spacecraft with a crew of three in October of 1964. America managed two (Grissom and Young) in March of 1965. Cosmonaut Alexei Leonov performed the first spacewalk on March 18, 1965, and astronaut Ed White followed up with America's first EVA on June 3rd of that year. The US appeared to be permanently fixed in the runner-up slot of the space race.

AMERICA FINALLY GETS IT TOGETHER IN SPACE

America's second-generation spacecraft was designed to carry two crew members and demonstrate the ability to dock two spacecraft on orbit. Gemini 3, the previously mentioned Grissom and Young flight, was the program's first crewed mission. NASA had planned for Gemini 6 to dock with an unmanned Agena target vehicle in October of 1965. Wally Schirra and Thomas Stafford boarded their capsule and waited for the Agena to launch. However, the Agena exploded immediately after separating from its Atlas booster.

Following such a dramatic failure, one would have expected a risk-averse NASA to stand down and wait for the Soviets to beat them at docking before trying again. Instead, the agency pivoted and aggressively pushed forward to at least demonstrate the ability to rendezvous in space, approaching another spacecraft in orbit and maintaining close station keeping. On December 12, Schirra and Stafford again took their seats in Gemini 6, now renamed 6A, and prepared for launch. The engines on their Titan II launch vehicle ignited and…1.5 seconds later shut down. Ignoring the official protocol for a failed launch, Schirra did not pull the ring that would have ejected Stafford and himself from the capsule.[ii] NASA did some quick fixes and launched the two into space just three days later! Seven hours later, they made radar contact with Gemini 7, already in orbit and crewed by Frank Borman and Jim Lovell. The two Gemini capsules approached as close as thirty centimeters (one foot) and performed a series of approaches and fly-around inspections.

On March 16, 1966, Neil Armstrong and David Scott successfully docked their Gemini 8 spacecraft with an unmanned

ii   Later consideration suggested ejecting would have likely killed the two. Making a low-altitude parachute landing from just off the launch pad would have been very dangerous, and the capsule's pure oxygen environment would have erupted into flames the moment the seat ejectors ignited.

Agena target. A problem with a stuck thruster pushed the spacecraft into a high-g spin, nearly killing the two. However, Armstrong's remarkable performance under pressure saved the mission and contributed to his selection as commander of the Apollo 11 mission. Gemini missions continued on schedule, with four more completed that year.

This was a bold new NASA, ready to move aggressively to best the commies in space. What changed? Perhaps it was the frustration of the astronauts, but more likely, the agency was feeling heat from Congress and the White House. With the Vietnam War escalating and President Johnson launching expensive social programs at home, spending billions to be second place in space was getting hard to sell.

SOYUZ

At this time, Korolev was working on their third-generation space system, dubbed "Soyuz" (Союз). The name, which means "Union," applied both to the rocket and spacecraft it carried. While Soyuz would turn out to be the longest-running human space flight program—there is one docked at the International Space Station today—it had a rocky start. Russia had found itself a problem child that would derail their leadership position.

Sergei Korolev died during a botched surgery in 1966, and the Soviet space program was in tatters. There was a two-year gap before the first Soyuz missions, Soyuz 1 and 2, were ready to launch and attempt an orbital rendezvous in April of 1967. The sole occupant of Soyuz 1, Vladimir Komarov, was killed when the parachutes of his reentry modules failed to properly deploy.[204] This resulted in another eighteen-month delay. A docking between Soyuz 2 and 3 failed. Soyuz 4 and 5 were finally docked in January of 1969, years after the Americans.[205] Korolev's big N1 Moon rocket suffered a series of spectacular launch failures,[206] ensuring that Russians would not walk on the Moon first or ever.

KENNEDY PROMISES US THE MOON

Following the debacle of the Bay of Pigs, an April 1961 American-backed invasion of communist Cuba, President Kennedy had turned to space looking for a way to best the Soviets. Von Braun advised the young president that America could very publicly beat the Russians by sending a man to the Moon and returning him safely to Earth.[207]

Kennedy took this to heart and proposed the Moon project in a "Special Message to Congress on Urgent National Needs" on May 25, 1961.[208] In it, he clearly laid out American strategy on this point: "No single space project in this period will be more impressive to mankind, or more important for the long-range exploration of space; and none will be so difficult or expensive to accomplish."

It was important that the cost and technical complexity of such a program would strain the Soviets. The challenge America faced was building a rocket big enough to do the job. Size was the one area where Korolev and his team held an advantage. This situation worked out perfectly for von Braun, as it satisfied his personal goals and fulfilled the dreams of all his companions in that long-ago German rocket craze, to send people to the Moon. He also had a very big rocket, in his pocket, the Saturn.

While Kennedy's speech (quoted in our chapter opening) at Rice University the following year energized a generation of youthful dreamers, many practical observers believed that we had "more important problems here on Earth" and that the program was unlikely to succeed, at least in its audacious schedule of "sending an American safely to the Moon before the end of the decade." It may have been the martyrdom of the charismatic young president that protected his program and allowed it to consume more than $20 billion in federal funding, over $150 billion in Biden-era dollars. In the mid-1960s, the space program was consuming more than 4 percent of the federal budget,[209] an order of magnitude greater than its position today.[210]

VON BRAUN'S BIG ROCKET

Back at the Army's Redstone Arsenal in Huntsville, Alabama, Wernher von Braun was building a massive rocket on the scale of the Soviets' N1. Whereas the Soviets' plan was to use a lot of engines—thirty-three on the first stage—von Braun's Saturn V would use just five. What they lacked in quantity, the Rocketdyne's F-1 engines made up in size and power. Standing eighteen feet tall and delivering over 1.5 million pounds of thrust, these are still the most powerful rocket engines ever built. The Russians couldn't build anything this big and were forced into their much more complex design. The Saturn V in total was a massive three-stage rocket standing over 100 meters (360 feet) tall and weighing in at six and a half million pounds.

APOLLO 1

Seneca the Younger wrote, "There is no easy way from Earth to the Stars,"[iii] and the road to success on the Moon was not

---

iii Spoken by Megara, Hercules's wife. In the original Latin, "non est ad astra mollis e terris via."

as easy as it appears in hindsight. On January 27, 1967, Gus Grissom, Edward White, and Roger Chaffee rode the elevator up the launch tower at Pad 34 (now SLC 34 at Cape Canaveral Space Force Station), crossed the access arm, and climbed into their Apollo 1 capsule. They were sealed in and commenced conducting a "plugs out" test of the systems running on internal power. A short in one of the electrical connectors sparked a fire that quickly spread inside the cabin's pure oxygen atmosphere. The complexity of the latching mechanism and the higher pressure inside the capsule made it impossible to open the hatch. All three astronauts were engulfed in flames and smoke, and they perished in agony while those outside listened to the radio in horror. It was the first fatal disaster in the history of US space flight.[211]

America's lunar program continued apace while the technical causes of the fire were addressed. Flammable materials were removed, the door hatches were reengineered, and the pure oxygen environment was replaced with normal air. NASA showed a sense of urgency that would be absent in the agency's responses to the loss of *Challenger* and *Columbia*. Von Braun's big rocket, the Saturn V, would launch an uncrewed Apollo capsule later that year, and crewed flights resumed at a brisk pace late the next year. Frank Borman, James Lovell, and William Anders spent Christmas Eve of 1968 orbiting the Moon and reading passages from the Book of Genesis in a live broadcast to Earth. Borman closed with, "a Merry Christmas and God bless all of you—all of you on the good Earth." For the officially atheist leaders of the Soviet Union, this was a very poignant message indeed.

Apollo 9 would test the delicate Lunar Excursion Module (LEM). Apollo 10 commander Tom Stafford would fly his

LEM, "Snoopy," to within 14.4 kilometers (7.8 nautical miles) of the Moon's surface. Worried that Stafford and his pilot, Gene Cernan, might attempt an unauthorized landing, NASA had insured against that. Cernan noted:

> A lot of people thought about the kind of people we were: "Don't give those guys an opportunity to land, 'cause they might!" So the ascent module, the part we lifted off the lunar surface with, was short-fueled. The fuel tanks weren't full. So had we literally tried to land on the Moon, we couldn't have gotten off.[212]

TRANQUILITY BASE HERE. THE EAGLE HAS LANDED.

On July 20, 1969, Kennedy's expensive Moon gamble paid off. Americans spent that Sunday at home, "glued to the tube," watching a fuzzy black and white video feed of Neil Armstrong descending the ladder of the fragile lunar lander, Eagle, and putting his foot into the dust of another world.

Even though Armstrong dropped an "a" from his memorized line, "That's one small step for [a] man, one giant leap for mankind," it still ranks among the most quoted statements in history.[iv, 213] Walter Cronkite, the most trusted man in America, enthused like a kid, "Man on the Moon!…Oh, boy…Whew, boy!" Over six hundred million people around the world watched what BBC has termed "the greatest single

---

iv   While there has been some debate over whether the "a" was lost in a transmission glitch to Earth, Buzz Aldrin confirmed in conversation with one of your authors (Autry) that he did not hear the "a" on the clear, local circuit. The Smithsonian, based on waveform analysis, accepts it was not there.

broadcast in television history." Our nation was admired more for Apollo than for any other achievement in its history. Soviet technology would forever be viewed as second-rate in the eyes of the world, and communism seemed to lose the luster it had once held for globalist intellectuals. Losing the Moon race was also highly demoralizing for Russian morale, and the long decline that led to the final collapse of the Soviet Union might best be dated from the summer of '69.

Five more Apollo missions would successfully land on the Moon and return their crews safely to Earth. Even the near disaster of Apollo 13, which was forced to abort its landing and limp home, became a triumph of American engineering and derring-do, and, thanks to Hollywood, enshrined the phrase "Failure is not an option" in our national lexicon.[214]

THE END OF APOLLO

When Richard Milhous Nixon took the oath of office on January 20, 1969, he faced one of the most troubled times in American history. Martin Luther King and Bobby Kennedy had been assassinated the year before. America was losing Johnson's war in Vietnam and nobody wanted to fight it. Riots roiled our cities and college campuses, and tensions in the Middle East were high. Johnson's domestic programs were busting the budget, and the Hong Kong flu pandemic was busy killing over one hundred thousand Americans. Even though he was to a great extent personally responsible for NASA's genesis (as Eisenhower's VP), space must have been one of the last things on Nixon's mind.

NASA had missions planned through Apollo 20, but Nixon was less sure. Following the enormous success of

Apollo 15, with a multiday stay on the Moon and use of a lunar rover to cover more ground, Nixon considered declaring victory and cancelling all of the remaining missions. He was clearly motivated to save money, and there was a fear that if the program was extended too long, someone was sure to die on the Moon.[215] Caspar Weinberger, deputy director of the Office of Management and Budget, talked him into keeping two more landings.

> Recent Apollo flights have been very successful from all points of view. Most important is the fact that they give the American people a much-needed lift in spirit, (and the people of the world an equally needed look at American superiority). Announcement now, or very shortly, that we were cancelling Apollo 16 and 17 (an announcement we would have to make very soon if any real savings are to be realized) would have a very bad effect, coming so soon after Apollo 15's triumph. It would be confirming, in some respects, a belief that I fear is gaining credence at home and abroad: That our best years are behind us, that we are turning inward, reducing our defense commitments, and voluntarily starting to give up our super-power status, and our desire to maintain world superiority....[216]

The last flight of an Apollo capsule came in 1975 with a US–USSR joint mission in space. While Apollo-Soyuz did a little science, its "handshake in space" moment was designed as a showpiece for Cold War détente.[217]

NASA was working on several other big projects including lunar bases and camper vans, incredibly powerful (and safe) nuclear rockets, a space station, and a reusable spaceplane that would become the Space Shuttle. The Moon was abandoned. So were the extremely promising nuclear rockets that had actually been successfully tested and might have gotten us to Mars in the 1980s. The shuttle and space stations would have to be "the future," and it would leave us stuck in low Earth orbit for two generations.

LESSONS LEARNED: LEADERSHIP AND RISK TOLERANCE ARE NECESSARY

Kennedy's charismatic leadership and willingness to sign on to the incredibly risky proposition of going to the Moon was the essential element in winning Space Race 1.0 and undermining the appeal of the Soviet system. In the end game against that evil empire, Ronald Reagan would make a similarly audacious commitment with his Strategic Defense Initiative (aka "Star Wars"). It turned out that this space defense system didn't really have to be developed in order to move Soviet leader Gorbachev to decide that the Americans were unbeatable. Star Wars has often been cited as a factor in the economic collapse of the Soviet Union and in their willingness to pursue a more cooperative path.

In facing China today, nothing will suffice for America but a bigger, better, and faster space program. Falling into second place would embolden their efforts to ensure more developing countries into their authoritarian fold. America must continue the bold space agenda established by the Trump White House and which has continued to receive strong bipartisan support. In particular, we must return to the Moon to stay. We cannot leave the prime real estate on our celestial neighbor in the hands of a Chinese–Russian partnership.

CHAPTER FOUR

A LONG INTERLUDE IN LEO: SHUTTLES AND SPACE STATIONS

As soon as somebody demonstrates the art of flying,
settlers from our species of man will not be lacking
[on the Moon and Jupiter]...Given ships or sails
adapted to the breezes of heaven, there will be those
who will not shrink from even that vast expanse.
—Johannes Kepler, letter to Galileo, 1610

A merica's spaceplane was an incredible feat of engineering. Formally known as the Space Transportation System (STS), the Space Shuttle combined vertical launch with the ability of the X-15 to land on a normal runway. The shuttle orbiter itself was 122 ft (37 m) long and weighed in at 240,000 lb (110,000 kg) in dry mass. It could loft itself, a crew of eight, and up to 35,000 lb (16,000 kg) to the space station. Most importantly, the shuttle was designed to be a mostly *reusable* system.

SORTA REUSABLE

Before the shuttle, every single rocket and every single spacecraft *flew just once*. It is best if discarded rocket bodies fall onto unpopulated areas, usually to the east of the launch site. An object sitting on Earth's equator is already moving eastward at over 1,000 mph (1,600 kmh)! Launching to the east, from a low-latitude site, increases launch performance by more than 5 percent, increasing the payload delivery capacity of all rockets. This is why Jules Verne knew an American Moon launch would be from Florida. A shuttle launched from Cape Canaveral, Florida, is gifted with 1,470 kmh, or 913 mph, of free velocity.

The US launches eastward from Cape Canaveral in Florida and Wallops Island in Virginia. For polar orbits, rockets fly south, over the Pacific, from Vandenberg Space Force Base in central California or from Alaska's Kodiak Island. The Soviets' Baikonur Cosmodrome in Kazakhstan offers a wilderness stretching east to Siberia. China also started their launch operations in an occupied nation at their Jiuquan Satellite Launch Center in Mongolia's vast Gobi Desert. China's Xichang Satellite Launch Center, added in the 1980s, routinely drops dangerous rocket boosters containing toxic chemicals onto towns and farmland in Sichuan province.[218]

SLOWER, WORSE, EXPENSIVER[i]

Reuse was supposed to make shuttles less expensive to operate. You'd fuel it, launch it, bring it back, refuel it, and fly again, just like an aircraft. The shuttle orbiter would be fully

---

i   We are having a little fun here with NASA's "Faster, Better, Cheaper" initiative from the 1990s, which has been blamed for a series of failures that occurred in the planetary exploration program at that time.

reusable and included three RS-25 engines for the system. These titanium beauties burned liquid hydrogen and liquid oxygen and were perhaps the most elegant and most efficient rocket engines ever built. The propellants were stored in a large external tank mounted to the bottom of the orbiter, though it looked as if the orbiter were riding on the tank. The tanks were disposable. On the sides were two large solid rocket boosters (SRBs). The shells of these could be recovered from the ocean, refurbished, and reused.

NASA expected to fly shuttles every two weeks and told Congress that each mission would cost only $10 million. Payload costs were to be as low as $100/lb ($250/kg) in 1972 dollars,[219] orders of magnitude cheaper than prevailing launch rates of $50,000 to $100,0000 per pound. It would almost be cheaper than international express package delivery.

Sadly, that never happened. The shuttle, while a miracle of technology and a thing of beauty, was enormously complex, surprisingly unreliable, and outright dangerous. In the end, a shuttle flight cost about $1.5 billion.[220] It never flew more than nine times in a year, and some years the program made no flights.[221] Worse, sixteen astronauts died in the tragic losses of the *Challenger* on liftoff in 1986 and of *Columbia* on reentry in 2003. What went wrong?

The economics of reuse never materialized. NASA gave up refurbishing the SRBs very early on because of salt corrosion and cost. The RS-25s needed a lot more servicing between flights than expected. The ceramic tiles that protected the shuttle needed constant replacement, and each was painstakingly unique. John M. Logsdon wrote, "There was a significant degree of technological hubris in NASA's view of what would be achievable."[222] Basically, NASA's engineers saw that a winged spacecraft could be built. What they did not envision was the additional requirements of well-meaning policy makers, the revenue-seeking nature of the aerospace contractors, and the bureaucracy of the state. Among the biggest mistakes was NASA convincing the DoD that the shuttle would provide them with regular and inexpensive space launch. The DoD was fond of polar orbits, and the US Air Force built out a shuttle launch facility at Vandenberg Air Force Base in California for that purpose.[223] Requiring the shuttle to be able to return to Vandenberg after a single orbit increased its wing size, drag, and thereby launch power requirements.[224]

The military shuttle plan was aborted in 1986, following the *Challenger* disaster. The complexity of the shuttle increased costs and reduced flight cadence. Accidents made this worse. Flights were halted for three years following each of the shuttle disasters while NASA and congressional investigations found faults, pointed fingers, and engineers fixed things.

BURAN

The complexity and expense of the Space Shuttle did not stop the Soviets from envying it. They built a copy of it, right down to its oversized wings and unique black and white livery. The copy was so specific that a quick glance at the Buran ("snowstorm") leaves most people thinking they are looking at an American Space Shuttle. Sadly, it flew just once, in 1988, taking off and landing under remote control, without a crew. Buran was an expensive system for a nation undergoing an economic collapse, and being a blatant copy of stolen American plans, it got little love from the Soviet aerospace community. Post-Soviet Russia officially killed the program and continued with Soyuz.[225]

ALL WINGED UP AND NOWHERE TO GO

Enterprise, the prototype shuttle, only made test glides after being lofted by a Boeing 747 carrier plane. *Columbia* made the first shuttle flight to space in 1981. *Challenger, Discovery*, and *Atlantis* soon joined her. Following the loss of the *Challenger* in 1986, Congress funded a replacement, *Endeavour*. So, America had a fleet of spaceplanes! Where could we go?

The answer turned out to be "round and round, but nowhere new." The shuttle could go up a few hundred miles and orbit Earth for a couple of weeks. The highest shuttle flight was about 600 km (375 mi) to deploy and later service the Hubble Space Telescope.[226] Hubble was initially deployed by *Discovery* in 1990 but turned out to have a serious defect in its mirror. Three years later, *Endeavour* installed a corrective "eyeglass" on the telescope. The Hubble servicing mission demonstrated that astronauts could do useful work in space, making the idea of a large, multicomponent space station more legitimate. That was good because the shuttle was transportation in search of a destination.

MOL, SALYUT, AND SKYLAB: EARLY SPACE STATIONS

Wernher von Braun had proposed an orbiting American space station in his 1947 speech in El Paso. Appropriate to the venue of a Rotary Club, his vision was of a wheel in space that eventually inspired the iconic Space Station V in Stanley Kubrick's 1969 film, *2001: A Space Odyssey*.

The first serious effort at a space station was the Air Force's Manned Orbiting Laboratory (MOL). The MOL was a single-use station developed for month-long stays in polar orbits. Inside the MOL, Air Force astronauts would secretly perform reconnaissance missions while outwardly conducting science experiments. They would access the station via a modified NASA Gemini capsule. A test fight in November of 1966 launched a MOL mock-up and Gemini B capsule. A pad was prepared at Vandenberg AFB, and seventeen astronauts were selected for missions. Budget pressures and improving automated spy satellites made the complexity and unreliability of humans less attractive to intelligence experts, and the program was terminated.[227]

The Soviets launched the world's first space station, Salyut 1, in 1971. Salyut ("salute") was a nominally civilian project based on a military design called "Almaz" ("diamond"). Salyut/Almaz stations were cylinders about 20 meters long (66 ft) and 4 meters wide (13 ft) containing about 100 cubic meters (3,500 ft.³) of pressurized space.[228]

The early Salyut program was as cursed as Soyuz had been. The first crew to visit Salyut 1 was unable achieve a secure docking and enter the station. A second crew got into the station and spent twenty-three days on board, but sadly, all three died when their Soyuz capsule leaked during the return. Salyut 2 was damaged by debris created from the failure of the second stage of its launch vehicle, and it crashed into the Pacific.

Meanwhile, the US had a space station plan as well. Skylab was a huge cylinder built out of the third stage of a Saturn V rocket. Skylab had more than three times the volume of a Salyut. There was plenty of room for astronauts to literally tumble around the space. The station was launched in May of 1973, and after a glitch with the solar arrays and heat shield was fixed, it worked well. It hosted visits from three Apollo capsules, each with three crew members. The final crew spent eighty-four days in space, trouncing the Soviet space station numbers in every way.[229]

NASA had planned for Skylab to stay up until the Space Shuttle was ready to visit it and reboost it to a higher orbit. Unfortunately, the shuttle was late, and increased solar activity pushed Skylab down into Earth's atmosphere sooner than expected. Parts of Skylab landed in southwest Australia in 1979.[230] The local authorities in the Shire of Esperance issued NASA a fine of $400 for littering.[231]

Salyut 3 (Almaz 2) was a Soviet military space station launched in 1974. The Soviets equipped this one with a fourteen-millimeter repeating cannon and planned to add interceptor missiles to future versions.[232] Thankfully, the Soviet brass concluded that space reconnaissance was better accomplished robotically.

MIR, ISS, TIANGONG, AND GATEWAY: MODULAR SPACE STATIONS

The first really long-term space stations were Salyut 6 and 7. Each lasted for several years and hosted dozens of cosmonauts. The next generation of Salyuts would be built to allow for additional modules. These would be the cores for two remarkable future stations.

The core module of the Mir ("peace") station was launched in 1986, and the first crew visited it and Salyut 7 during the same mission. The important thing about Mir was that it was a modular station, with new sections being added over a ten-year construction period. Mir hosted the longest duration space flight of 438 days.[233]

After the fall of the Soviet Union, the US saw an opportunity to play nice with Russia and give the shuttle a destination. Nine shuttle missions docked with Mir.[234] This partnership laid the groundwork for something much bigger.

While Mir was being built, NASA began pushing for a space station of their own. In his 1984 State of the Union address, President Reagan had announced the development of "a permanently manned space station" to be completed by 1990, with this vision:

> A space station will permit quantum leaps in our research in science, communications, in metals, and in lifesaving medicines which could be manufactured only in space. We want our friends to help us meet these challenges and share in their benefits. NASA will invite other countries to participate so we can strengthen peace, build prosperity, and expand freedom for all who share our goals.

NASA established a Space Station Program Office in Houston the next year. In 1988, the president announced the station would be named "Freedom." Japan, Canada, and the European Space Agency signed on to the project. The ambitious station was constantly undergoing redesigns to accommodate budget shortfalls and fell behind schedule. In 1993, the Clinton administration invited the new Russian Republic to join the project. It was renamed the International Space

Station (ISS), commonly referred to by space insiders as simply "station."[235]

In 1998, Russians lofted the backup core for Mir, renamed "Zarya" ("sunrise"), and the ISS was underway. Just three weeks later, the Space Shuttle *Endeavour* delivered the first American module, Unity. More modules followed, and on Halloween day 2000, the first crew of two cosmonauts and one American arrived in a Soyuz capsule and began the permanent occupation of the station. [236] The station continued to expand, using Russian, American, and Japanese modules. Today, the ISS has a mass of nearly one million pounds and provides over one thousand cubic meters of pressurized interior space, about the same as a Boeing 747 aircraft. Its huge solar panels can generate nearly 250 kilowatts of power,[237] which is equivalent to about forty home solar installations.

Building and operating the ISS has demonstrated amazing engineering skill and international cooperation. However, don't let the "international" part fool you into thinking that cooperation extends to station finances. Out of the $150 billion spent on the ISS to date, over $125 billion of that has been paid for by the US taxpayer.[238] This includes shuttle flights to the station, paying the Russians for their first module, for modifying their Soyuz TMA vehicle to accommodate non-Russian astronauts, and for flying US astronauts and those of other nations on Soyuz. The annual $3.1 billion operation and maintenance bill for the station is basically entirely paid by NASA.[239] The European contribution to the ISS upkeep was waived in exchange for their developing a service module for the Orion capsule, which is odd since they get public credit for both projects.[240]

Nothing lasts forever, and the ISS is no exception. Many components, particularly in the Russian segment, are showing their age. Additionally, NASA is returning to the Moon, and its budget must go there as well. The station is currently scheduled to be retired in 2030. NASA will maintain its presence in low Earth orbit as an anchor tenant on soon to be launched commercial space stations known as "Commercial LEO Destinations" or CLDs.[ii]

So, what do you do with the "most expensive thing ever built"? If you're NASA, you apparently dump it into a spot in the South Pacific affectionately named "Point Nemo."[241] Originally, this was going to be done with three Russian Progress vehicles for about $300 million.[242] Yep, American taxpayers were going to pay Russia, again. With the Russian government and its space hardware becoming increasingly unreliable, NASA has decided they needed a US deorbit vehicle (USDV) and posted a request for proposal (RFP) in May of 2023 for up to $1 billion. NASA modified the production contract from "firm fixed price" to allowing for "cost plus," which historically suggests the price will get much higher.[243]

Your coauthor, Greg Autry, has argued that the ISS is worth saving[244] as a historical artifact and that lofting it safely up to a higher orbit can be done in the same cost range as the deorbit plan. More importantly, the investment should be used to create a commercial "space tug" with capabilities that will benefit NASA, the DoD, and commercial operators in the future.[245]

Naturally, if everyone else has one, China needs a space station. The communist nation has been precluded from joining the ISS by the 2011 Wolf Amendment that prohibits NASA from using any federal funds to engage with the

---

ii   You gotta love NASA for creating acronyms that have other acronyms inside them. LOL.

Chinese government or its state-owned enterprises.[246] That's a very necessary thing, given their rapacious appetite for stealing American technology. So, they have developed their own station named "Tiangong." The Chinese station, which received its first crew in 2021, is about one-tenth the size of the ISS but is modular and growing. Its module count may double from three to six in the next few years.[247] Most significantly, the Chinese are using Tiangong as a platform to engage other nations. The BBC reported that "China hopes Tiangong will replace the International Space Station" when NASA drops the ISS into Point Nemo.[248] The European Space Agency (ESA) began training astronauts to fly to the Chinese station but wisely suspended that decision in 2023.[249] China is now exploring opportunities with several Arab nations.[250]

NASA hasn't exited the space station business. They are in the process of building the next one, a smaller, maneuverable station called "Gateway." This will also be an international project, with modules from Japan and Europe, along with the ubiquitous robotic Canadarm. India may contribute as well.[251] Gateway is highly mobile within cis-lunar space but will initially be positioned in a special near-rectilinear halo orbit (NRHO) near Lagrange Point 2 on the far side of the Moon to support the upcoming Artemis landings on the Moon.[252]

AFTER THE SHUTTLE

In 2004, President Bush made the decision to retire the Space Shuttle as part of his "Vision for Space Exploration."[253] Bush later proposed a new program called "Constellation" that would return America to the Moon using a large Ares V cargo rocket and a smaller Ares I human-rated rocket. There would be a new, larger Apollo-style capsule called "Orion."[254] President Obama cancelled Bush's vision and the Ares rockets in 2010.[255] With the Space Shuttle winding down to retirement in 2012, the US needed a new solution for human space flight and particularly for getting Americans to and from the ISS.

TRAMPOLINES AND BROOMSTICKS

After the shuttle made its last flight in 2011, and the shuttles were sent off to museums, the only way for American astronauts to reach our $100 billion space station was to pay the Russians for a ride. NASA had already paid for upgrading their Soyuz capsule to the TMA version, which added modern digital controls and adjustable seats capable of accommodating the varying sizes of American astronauts.[256] In the old Soviet system, cosmonauts were fitted to the spacecraft rather than the other way round.

Seeing an opportunity for exploitation, Russia raised the per-seat cost for NASA astronauts from just over $20 million in 2007 to over $80 million in 2012.[257] When the Obama administration levied sanctions against the Putin regime in response to the 2014 Russian invasion of Crimea, Russia's deputy prime minister Dmitry Rogozin tweeted:

> After reviewing the sanctions against our [Russian space industry], [I] suggest [that the] United States deliver their astronauts to the ISS [International Space Station] using a trampoline.[258]

In 2022, after President Biden announced sanctions over the Russian attack on Ukraine, Rogozin, now the head of the

Russian space agency, Roscosmos, halted sales of rocket components to US firms and told a state-run TV station:

> In a situation like this, we can't supply the United States with our world's best rocket engines. Let them fly on something else, their broomsticks, I don't know what.[259]

By that time however, America had a very cool new "broomstick," and we no longer required Russian flights or engines. Dmitry was now the joke....

LESSONS LEARNED: COMPETITION BEATS COOPERATION

International partnerships are powerful geopolitical tools but can also be potential traps. While the competition of Space Race 1.0 drove America forward at light speed, the cooperation of détente slowed progress immensely, leaving us unprepared and exposed when our partner Russia shifted gears and surprised as China emerged as a peer competitor. We must see this challenge as a motivation to dare even greater things.

We must retain that competitive spirit and achieve great things with our allies in the Artemis Accords, an international accord launched during the Trump administration. We must also seek even greater contributions from our most capable free world space allies—Japan, Canada, Europe, and the UK.

CHAPTER THREE

THE CRAZY ONES AND WACKY PEOPLE: ENTREPRENEURS AND DREAMERS RESHAPE OUR FUTURE IN SPACE

Here's to the crazy ones. The misfits. The rebels. The troublemakers. The round pegs in the square holes. The ones who see things differently. They're not fond of rules. And they have no respect for the status quo. You can quote them, disagree with them, glorify or vilify them.

But the only thing you can't do is ignore them. Because they change things. They invent. They imagine. They heal. They explore. They create. They inspire. They push the human race forward. Maybe they have to be crazy.

While some see them as the crazy ones, we see genius. Because the people who are crazy enough to think they can change the world, are the ones who do.

—Apple "Think Different" commercial, 1996[i]

Those of us old enough to have watched Neil and Buzz walk on the Moon and who watched *2001: A Space Odyssey* on a Cinerama screen[ii] expected to be walking on the Moon or getting our ride to that wheel in space. Millennials and Zoomers raised on technology have expectations of constant progress. Nearly everyone in the space community has been frustrated by the lack of substantial progress in space since the demise of Apollo. Today, a few bold dreamers are doing something about that. Free markets and entrepreneurship are America's real space weapons.

THE GOVERNMENT VS. THE CRAZY ONES

Getting to space, going to the Moon, and building space stations required massive capital and coordination of national resources. It is highly unlikely that any private effort would have gotten us there in our lifetimes. In the 1960s, the US government spent an enormous amount of money to achieve legitimate geopolitical and military objectives in space that helped us win the Cold War without a shot being fired. However, in the absence of a crisis, the US government has always retreated from bold action. The government is also far from being an economically efficient actor. While operating gov-

i   Written primarily by Rob Siltanen and Ken Segall of TBWA\Chiat\Day with input from Steve Jobs.

ii   A wide-screen movie format of the 1960s. The film *2001* was actually shot in Panavision 70.

ernmental systems like the Space Shuttle and the ISS inevitably turns out to be too expensive for economic sustainability, the government is almost never willing to let go of a program.

The dawn of the new millennium revealed a 2001 that did not look like *2001*. Where the hell was our Pan Am flight to Space Station V? Outside of transcontinental telecommunications and satellite television, the business cases for space would not close with the government driving the costs of space launch and satellite construction. Doing it cheaper was technically possible, as the designers of the Space Shuttle knew, but the big space firms of the military-industrial complex lacked any motivation to work on cost reduction. Aerospace contractors had a good thing going with the government. They usually worked on "cost plus" contracts, where their profits were guaranteed regardless of how well or how badly managed their efforts were. This made formerly disruptive firms like Boeing and Lockheed reluctant to invest shareholder capital in risky commercial endeavors. Why should they? They solved big hairy problems, and they built truly amazing things, but not at the speeds and prices required to satisfy the demands of the private sector. Consequently, progress to reduce costs and increase access to space has been driven by entrepreneurs, most of them more than a little bit crazy.

A STUNTMAN AND A FRUITCAKE

Robert Craig Knievel was as crazy as they come. The self-promoting stuntman, known to the public as "Evel Knievel," was famous for trying to jump Harley-Davidson motorcycles over cars, buses, fountains, and even tanks filled with live sharks.

In the process, he suffered an extensive list of broken bones. Knievel's biggest dream had always been to jump over the Grand Canyon. Unsurprisingly, the US Department of the Interior had jurisdiction over most of the canyon and did not share the stuntman's enthusiasm with killing himself on federal land. Alluding to another passion of his, Evel used a 1968 interview in *Sports Illustrated* to respond to his detractors:

> I don't care if they say, 'Look, kid, you're going
> to drive that thing off the edge of the Canyon
> and die,' I'm going to do it. I want to be the
> first. If they'd let me go to the moon, I'd crawl
> all the way to Cape Kennedy just to do it. I'd
> like to go to the moon, but I don't want to be
> the second man to go there.[260]

Knievel moved his sights to Idaho's Snake River Canyon. He selected a 1,600-foot gap downstream from Hell's Canyon and leased land on which to conduct the stunt. Now all he needed was a motorcycle that could make the leap. His previous longest attempt, a failure at Caesar's Palace, was just 141 feet. It would take a rocket to cross that canyon.

Robert "Bob" Truax was a young naval officer inspired by the work of Robert Goddard. In the 1930s, he began building his own rockets and liquid-fueled rocket engines. During his career in the military, Truax led the teams that developed the first hypergolic (self-igniting) propellants, the JATO (rocket-assisted take-off packs for planes), and worked on the Polaris missile. Moving to the private sector, Truax headed design of Aerojet's Sea Dragon, a huge orbital rocket that would have launched from a silo afloat at sea. In 1966, he founded his own firm, Truax Engineering, with the crazy idea of pursing commercial rocket development outside the military-industrial complex.

Working on a project started by Doug Malewicki, Truax built the Skycycle X-2 for Evel Knievel's canyon jump. While the Skycycle did have two wheels, the vehicle was far more rocket than motorcycle. On the morning of September 8, 1974, Evel sat semi-recumbent inside a sleek aeroshell with large tail fins pointed skyward on a steeply inclined launch rail. A huge crowd had been gathering on the east side of the canyon for days. There was a party-like atmosphere filled with an eclectic mix of RV campers, motorcycle gangs, and hippies.[iii] Evel's steam-powered rocket vaulted into the air, leaving a white trail of steam against the blue Idaho sky. As the Skycycle climbed, its trajectory looked perfect, but partway across the canyon, the recovery parachute prematurely deployed. Evel and the Skycycle crashed into the canyon. Despite the failure, Truax's design was solid. In 2016, stuntman Eddie Braun flew a replica Skycycle X-2 named Evel Spirit across Snake River Canyon at 400 mph. The new Skycycle was built by Bob Truax's son, Scott.[261]

When Evel emerged from the canyon, bruised and battered but not seriously injured, he sauntered up to Truax and said, "Well Bob, that's going to be one hell of a hard act to follow. What else you got up your sleeve?"[262] Bob had a rocket up his sleeve.

Truax's real passion was his Project Private Enterprise, which would develop commercial space launch vehicles and fly paying "space tourists" on suborbital spaceflights above the

---

iii   Your coauthor, Greg Autry, attended the Snake River jump, as a twelve-year-old fan of Evel and of rockets.

fifty-mile limit on a vehicle called the "Volksrocket." Knievel agreed to give Truax a million bucks if the stuntman could become the first civilian in space. Unfortunately, Knievel's motorcycle jumping career was waning, and he failed to deliver more than a few thousand dollars for the rocket project. Truax, however, continued to pursue funding for his Volksrocket. Always having a sense of humor, he ran one ad titled, "Wanted: risky capital for risky project." The government had no interest in commercial spaceflight, and Truax remarked, "NASA doesn't talk to me. They think I'm nutty as a fruitcake."[263]

ADVENTURE, EXCITEMENT, AND REALLY WILD THINGS

Truax was the first but not the only starry-eyed fruitcake that NASA wouldn't talk to. The 1980s saw a number of credible space startups emerge. Texas real estate developer David Hannah Jr. came to believe that God wanted him to build a rocket. A 1982 *Texas Monthly* article quotes him as saying, "There's no question in my mind that I'm doing what the Lord wants me to do. What I don't know is whether He wants me to be successful."[264]

Hannah had been inspired by the writings of Gerard K. O'Neill, a Princeton physics professor who would implant the space settlement mind virus into an entire generation of otherwise rational people. O'Neill was convinced that someday millions of people would live and work inside of huge rotating structures in space, now referred to as O'Neill Cylinders. The concept of orbital space settlement is often referred to as "O'Neillian."[265] He pictured some of these destinations might be placed at the Earth–Moon Lagrange Point 5 and inspired an influential organization dedicated to promoting space settlement known as the L-5 Society.[266]

In December of 1979, Hannah found Gary C. Hudson, a twenty-nine-year-old college self-educated engineer with a passion for building commercial rockets. Hudson convinced Hannah he could build a truly private rocket. Hannah established Space Services, Incorporated of America (SSI or SSIA) and wrote a $200,000 check to Hudson's firm GCH, Inc. GCH would eventually raise about $1.2 million to build Percheron, a commercial rocket running the combination of kerosene and liquid oxygen commonly referred to as "kerolox." Hudson rented twenty thousand square feet of space in Sunnyvale, California, and recruited a band of eager engineers who weren't yet experienced enough to know what NASA and the big firms firmly believed: commercial spaceflight was not going to happen.[267] Nonetheless, they built a working rocket in just seven months and loaded it on a truck for Texas. Their big silver missile attracted a lot of attention, so they developed a cover story; they were transporting a "water heater." Detained by the New Mexico highway patrol, the truck driver took off and, according to *Texas Monthly*, managed "to elude an all-points bulletin all the way to Rockport."[268]

On August 5, 1981, Percheron was undergoing a preflight engine firing test on the pad at Matagorda Island, Texas, when it exploded in a spectacular ball of flame. Hannah missed the fireworks, but with God pushing him toward space, he marched on. Engineers at NASA's Johnson Space Center convinced Hannah to switch to easier to manage solid rocket motors. Hudson, who firmly believed that only liquid rockets would achieve the efficiencies necessary to support a commercial space economy, moved on.[269] SSIA hired former

Mercury astronaut Deke Slayton and obtained leftover ICBM missile stages to power their new Conestoga rockets. Conestoga 1 was launched from Matagorda on September 9, 1982, and ejected a dummy payload at 313 km, becoming the first privately funded rocket to reach space.[270] SSIA then attracted the first formal venture capital investment to a New Space firm with a $6 million placement from Ventures, Inc. However, those funds were withdrawn when attempts to commercialize Conestoga were delayed by "the regulatory environment and government policy."[271] The firm was sold to EER Systems.[272]

Nonetheless, EER/SSIA received some NASA support. In 1995, a four-stage, orbital version of the Conestoga, the 1620, was launched from NASA's Wallops Flight Facility in Virginia. However, the agency withdrew support after the rocket suffered a guidance problem and was destroyed in flight.[273]

In the early 1970s, Starstruck, a California startup, made three failed attempts at launching Dolphin. Their rocket was based on Truax's Sea Dragon floating launch silo concept and used a "hybrid" rocket motor with solid rubber or plastic as fuel and nitrous oxide an oxidizer.[274] Despite promising results on the final attempt, the company was unable to raise additional funding. Much of the original Starstruck team reemerged as AMROC, which eventually sold its hybrid motor technology to SpaceDev, Inc.[275]

In the late 1990s, Gary Hudson founded Rotary Rocket and set up operations at the Mojave Airport in California. Rotary attempted to build a rocket-powered helicopter, the Roton, capable of reaching space and landing for reuse. The firm attracted $30 million from a variety of sources including author Tom Clancy.[276] Test pilot Brian Binnie took the Roton on successful, low-altitude test flights down the runway at

Mojave.[277] However, funding struggles were exacerbated by licensing complexity and NASA hostility, and the firm failed.[278]

While commercial space launch has primarily been an American activity, once again, the Germans were the first movers. In 1974, Lutz Kayser, a German engineer, established Orbital Transport-und Raketen-Aktiengesellschaft (Orbital Transport and Rockets), or OTRAG, to develop a commercial rocket. Originally, Kurt Debus, former director of NASA's Kennedy Space Center, was chairman of the board, and Wernher von Braun served as an advisor. Despite opposition from these Americans, Kayser located his business in Zaire.[279] France and the USSR, both still fearful of German rockets, pressured Zaire and West Germany to shut OTRAG down. The team essentially fled to Libya in 1980, where Muammar Gaddafi eventually confiscated their facilities and equipment.[280]

In the 1990s, Texas developer and banker Andy Beal concluded that the space launch industry would be a good business. Beal saw that companies were planning to launch a lot of communications satellites. Motorola had announced their Iridium satellite phone system. Microsoft founder Bill Gates, telecom entrepreneur Craig McCaw, and Saudi prince Al Waleed bin Talal were backing a constellation of 840 satellites, in a startup called "Teledesic," which would give global customers access to the newly released internet.[281] Surely competing constellations would follow. Meanwhile, Boeing and Lockheed had cut investment into the development and operation of their traditional rockets because NASA and the DoD had essentially tried to put them out of business with the promise of cheap and frequent deliveries to space on the Space Shuttle. Since that hadn't worked, American satellite operators and even the US government were increasingly dependent on Europe, Russia, and China for space launch. Beal was fairly certain that a commercial US company could win back this market, and as a renowned high-stakes poker player,[iv] he was willing to bet very big.

Beal founded Beal Aerospace in 1997. Its rockets would utilize hydrogen peroxide as an oxidizer, eliminating the difficulties of handling cryogenic liquid oxygen, a choice that Elon Musk later said had doomed the endeavor.[282] The engines would also be pressure-fed by feeding helium gas into the tops of the propellant tanks rather than using more costly and complex turbopumps. A large engine test facility was built in McGregor, Texas.[283]

Still, NASA was far from supportive, and the DoD was financing the development of competing vehicles from their usual partners in the military-industrial complex.[284] Beal went to Congress and pleaded, "Please, please do not give companies billions of our dollars to play around with experimental programs. You will create jobs by spending public money, but you absolutely will not produce low-cost commercial access to space." A frustrated Beal shut his firm down in 2000, citing US government hostility toward commercial space endeavors.[285]

"NORMAL" PEOPLE IN SPACE

While the Volksrocket never got off the ground, the market that Bob Truax foresaw was real. Evel Knievel wasn't the only person willing to pay for a ride to space. What they required

---

iv Beal's winning of a record $11.7 million poker hand at the Bellagio in 2004 is detailed in Michael Craig's book *The Professor, the Banker, and the Suicide King: Inside the Richest Poker Game of All Time.*

was a proven spacecraft, and only two organizations could offer that: NASA and Roscosmos.

Charles Walker was rejected by NASA when he applied for the 1978 astronaut class, but he found another route to space. As a test engineer at McDonnell Douglas, Walker worked on experimental hardware for in-space pharmaceutical manufacturing that would be utilized by a Johnson & Johnson subsidiary. He supported the training of shuttle astronauts in the operation of these complex systems, and Douglas proposed that Walker should support experiments directly. NASA, still under the delusion that the Space Shuttle was an inexpensive flight system, charged McDonnell $40,000 to fly Walker as a "payload specialist" in April of 1984. He flew twice more the following year, a cadence that would make NASA astronauts jealous.[286] Walker was certainly not a "space tourist," but he could be classified as the first commercial astronaut.

NASA was also looking to use their safe and inexpensive new spacecraft to drum up public and congressional support. The agency designated Senator Jake Garn of Utah as a payload specialist and "congressional observer" and put him on a flight in April of 1985.[287] They flew Florida congressman Bill Nelson in 1986.[288] Nelson went on to become a US senator. In 2021, he was appointed to be the NASA administrator by his former Senate colleague, Joe Biden.[289]

As part of a public outreach campaign, NASA launched the Teacher in Space program and prepared to fly a civilian payload specialist, Christa McAuliffe. McAuliffe and six other astronauts perished when the Space Shuttle *Challenger* was destroyed shortly after liftoff on the cold morning of January 28, 1986.[290] NASA immediately ceased promotional flights.

The Soviets got busy with flying civilians as well, but being good communists, they were in it for profits. Tokyo Broadcasting System paid them approximately $10 million to fly Toyohiro Akiyama to the Mir space station in 1990.[291] Looking to get a Brit into space, a UK group raised funds from private donors and corporations to buy a ticket to space from the Soviets. Helen Sharman answered an ad reading, "Astronaut wanted. No experience necessary," and was selected as one of four candidates to receive cosmonaut training. Sharman was a PhD chemist who worked on developing chocolate candy flavoring for Mars. Sharman had no idea who would win the seat when she walked into a BBC studio for a live TV show that would announce Britain's first cosmonaut. Her prize appeared to be in jeopardy when the British fundraising came up short of the £7 million required, but Soviet president Mikhail Gorbachev personally intervened to support her mission.[292] The British press referred to the twenty-seven-year-old Sharman as the "girl from Mars" when she launched to Mir on May 18, 1991.[293]

The first self-funded space tourist, Dennis Tito, paid for a ride to the ISS in 2001.[294] Tito, who prefers the term "spaceflight participant," contracted his flight through a Virginia-based company, Space Adventures.[295] Tito said that Yuri Gagarin's flight to space inspired his "dream to fly in space before I die." At age sixty, he decided it was time to go and signed a deal with a private firm named MirCorp to fly a Soyuz to the aging ex-Soviet space station.

MirCorp was founded in 1999 by a group including space activist Rick Tumlinson and funded primarily by telecommunications entrepreneur and space enthusiast Walt Anderson. Another noted space entrepreneur, Jeff Manber, became Mir-

Corp CEO, and in February 2000, the company leased the unused station from the Russian government, which had moved on to the building of the ISS in a partnership with NASA. MirCorp paid for boosting the station and for a team of Russian cosmonauts to repair and restart it. A Progress cargo vehicle also arrived to restock the station.[296]

Everything was now ready for Tito...except for NASA. The American space agency didn't want a rival, commercial space station distracting the Russians or the public from their ISS program. NASA put pressure on Russia to withdraw from the Mir project. This induced hesitation in the investors, just as the NASDAQ "tech bubble" burst, leaving Anderson illiquid. Mir was deorbited in March of 2001, leaving Tito with nowhere to go.[297]

Tito was then able to shift his Russian ticket to the ISS through Space Adventures, a company founded by entrepreneur aerospace engineer Eric Anderson. The trip cost Tito $20 million. NASA was still not happy.[298] Administrator Dan Goldin viewed Tito as a dangerous distraction from the government's monopoly of running things in space. He commented, "Space is dangerous. It's not a joyride. Space is not about egos."[299] Bob Cabana, the ISS manager at NASA's Johnson Space Center, denied training to the entire Russian team in order to keep this pesky space tourist off of his station. When the Russians insisted that Tito was an integral part of their team, Cabana stated, "In that case, we will not be able to begin training, because we are not willing to train with Dennis Tito." The entire crew was denied access to NASA facilities to prevent an American civilian from flying.[300]

Russia flew Tito to the station anyway, and that opened the way for Space Adventures to fly several more private spaceflight participants to the ISS at prices that would eventually exceed $50 million. Ticket holders would include the first woman space tourist, Anousheh Ansari. Ansari, an Iranian American engineer and telecom entrepreneur, would be pivotal in another important space tourism first, which bears her family name, the Ansari X Prize.

WACKY SPACE COWBOY MAKES A BREAKTHROUGH

Meanwhile, back in the High Desert of California, legendary aircraft designer Burt Rutan was working on his next quixotic project. Rutan had revolutionized the low-end general aviation market with a line of composite aircraft kits that folks could assemble at home. He had been a civilian test pilot at Edwards Air Force Base during the '60s and had seen the X-15 in action. His firm, Scaled Composites, would build a less expensive, civilian version of that spaceplane to win a prize dreamed up by another wild-eyed space activist.

Peter Diamandis had always wanted to go to space and strategically prepared his career to be the ideal astronaut candidate. He obtained a master's in aeronautics and astronautics from MIT and an MD from Harvard. However, working with astronauts on projects at NASA's Johnson Space Center disillusioned him. During the shuttle era, things just moved too slowly. He told *Wired*, "I'm sick and tired of waiting."[301]

Looking at the events that had broken open aviation in the last century, Diamandis had discovered that Lindbergh and many others had made their risky record-setting flights in the pursuit of prize money. In one notable case, pineapple magnate James D. Dole, who desired quicker transportation from California to Hawaii, put up a $25,000 prize for the first air flight from Oakland to Honolulu. Two aircraft completed the 1927 Dole Air Race, six were lost or crashed, and ten people perished.

Diamandis decided to offer a $10 million prize for the first successful, reusable suborbital spacecraft. He announced his X-Prize at the National Space Society's International Space Development Conference in 1995. The biggest problem was that he didn't have $10 million. Diamandis convinced Anousheh Ansari and her family to pay the premiums for a Lloyd's of London "hole in one" insurance policy that would pay $10 million in the event of a private firm completing spaceflights by 2005.[302]

Rutan had the good fortune to find billionaire Microsoft cofounder Paul Allen. Allen, another space crazy entrepreneur, had previously rescued the Search for Extraterrestrial Intelligence (SETI) when Congress stopped funding the radio telescope program made famous by Jodie Foster in the film *Contact*.[303] Allen eventually put $24 million into Rutan's project, and by early 2004, Rutan had a revolutionary vehicle ready to go. Like the X-15, this system included a large carrier plane, White Knight, and a smaller rocket-powered spacecraft named SpaceShipOne. The spacecraft would be powered by hybrid motors from SpaceDev, technology inherited from the Dolphin project.

Rutan, like many disruptive entrepreneurs in the commercial space era, was an ardent libertarian who bristled at governmental bureaucracy. He dressed in the jeans, boots, and big belt buckles that signaled the independent attitude of High Desert "cowboy aviation." However, Rutan found his firm was able to establish a good relationship with the Federal Aviation Administration's Office of Commercial Space Transportation (FAA/AST). Upon accepting the FAA's license from Associate Administrator Patti Grace Smith, he turned to the audience and said, "Never let it be said that I don't kiss up to the government."[304] Stuart O. Witt, the CEO and general manager of the Mojave Airport, was instrumental in the success of the project and in getting Mojave licensed to conduct suborbital spaceflights as the nation's first inland spaceport.[305]

On the morning of June 21, 2004, SpaceShipOne was dropped from White Knight, and pilot/astronaut Mike Melville flew the little craft through the US fifty-mile limit and above the 100-km Kármán line at a top speed just shy of Mach 3. NASA's human spaceflight program was in the middle of a three-year hiatus induced by the *Columbia* disaster, and so Melville proudly posed with a large placard reading "SpaceShipOne, Government Zero." In September and October of that year, Melville and Brian Binnie would make two flights within a week and capture the X-Prize. SpaceShipOne is now on display at the National Air and Space Museum in Washington, DC.

For commercial space dreamers, the real win in the event came with Sir Richard Branson stepping up to a microphone and announcing the formation of a new company, Virgin Galactic, with his intent to purchase spacecraft built by Rutan in order to commercialize spaceflight for the masses.[306] Branson began selling tickets to space for just $200,000. That was two orders of magnitude less than Tito had paid and way lower than the going rate to the ISS, which had reached $52 million with soprano Sarah Brightman's purchase in 2012.[307] Remarking on the success and the eclectic nature of the those who brought it to fruition, Rutan said, "Usually the wacky people have the breakthroughs. The 'smart' people don't."[308]

LESSONS LEARNED: THINK DIFFERENT TO WIN

This story shows that leveraging the power of America's "crazy ones" and "wacky people" will be key to staying ahead of China in space. We will not beat China at socialism by running a centrally planned, governmental space race. We were able to do that with the Soviets in Space Race 1.0 because our nation was the "workshop to the world," and we could out-manufacture and outspend anyone. Space entrepreneur Jeff Greason (Rotary, XCOR) once remarked, "Apollo was essentially a public proof to the world that we could do communism better than the Russians."[309] However, several decades of mostly bad trade policy have transferred most of America's productive capacity and a lot of our wealth to our primary geopolitical adversary.

China's weakness remains innovation. While their communist system punishes people who dare to think different, our system (for better and worse) breeds disruptors. If we are going to win Space Race 2.0, we must out-innovate China and retain our capital and IP for use in growing our commercial sector. US industrial policy needs to support entrepreneurial efforts and encourage reinvestment in American aerospace manufacturing. We must rebuild a supply chain that can support both new startups and incumbent space manufacturers. Legislators, agencies, and regulators must be more failure tolerant. As this chapter shows, the crucible in which industries are forged burns up a lot of early risk takers.

CHAPTER TWO

COMMERCIAL SPACE ASCENDANT: MUSK, BEZOS, BRANSON, AND CAST OF THOUSANDS

Any time a great man tries to do a
wonderful thing, lesser men will try to stop
him. That is one of the laws of life.
—Frank Delaney, Ireland

The new millennium brought a trinity of wealthy and famous stars into the New Space constellation. Between 2000 and 2004, Amazon's Jeff Bezos, PayPal cofounder Elon Musk, and Virgin mogul Richard Branson each independently decided that it was time to launch a commercial spaceflight venture. It's difficult to believe that all three of these geniuses simultaneously lost their minds and their business acumen. Their efforts were supported and mirrored by dozens of lesser-known startups in a wave that emerged during the 2000s, swelled in the 2010s, and is cresting in the current decade.

THE OVERVIEW EFFECT

Bezos, Musk, and Branson share some key traits and motives. Firstly, they are each intuitively brilliant business strategists who have repeatedly run rings around powerful, established competitors in multiple fields. Secondly, they are rational risk takers who enjoy the rush of riding the edge of the wave. Most importantly, they are passionate. They always expect to make money, but one of the key reasons for their success is that profits are never their North Star. If they wanted to make money, space would surely not be their destination. As we've shown in the previous chapters, the road to the stars is littered with failed startups and bankrupt founders. A popular industry aphorism is, "The best way to be become a millionaire in the space business is to start as a billionaire." So why do this?

Beyond making money, each of these founders has expressed a desire to move humanity forward to a destiny beyond Earth and to expose more people to the "overview effect" for the benefit of our planet.[310] The overview effect is a cognitive disruption reported by many astronauts upon viewing Earth from space. It is a transformative sense of wonder and scale that brings them closer to Earth, to humanity, or to God. [311] Seeing a thin layer of atmosphere covering a planet where all of human history transpired instills a sense of awe, spiritual rededication, and even fear. Upon exiting one of Blue Origin's New Shepard spacecraft in 2021, actor William Shatner told Jeff Bezos, "What you have given me is the most profound experience. I hope I never recover from this."[312]

Bezos had been inspired by Gerard K. O'Neill when he was a student at Princeton and embraced the vision of millions of people living and working in space habitats. Musk had caught the space settlement bug from Robert Zubrin, the zealous author of *The Case for Mars* and founder of The Mars Society. The PayPal cofounder made it his life's goal to "occupy Mars."

In the summer of 2020, Sir Richard Branson beat Jeff Bezos to space in a flight aboard his own spacecraft. Branson had been inspired by the Moon landings and was a longtime aviation buff and adventurer. He has a passion for making the personal experience of spaceflight as good as it can be for as many people as possible.[313] Their firms reflect these similar but unique motivations.

FAILURE IS NOT AN OPTION; IT'S A REQUIREMENT

In the film *Apollo 13*, Ed Harris, portraying NASA flight director Gene Kranz, famously says, "We've never lost an American in space; we're sure as hell not going to lose one on my watch! Failure is not an option." Although the line was generated by the screenwriters, it was a true distillation of the spirit of that moment. NASA embraced it, and Kranz even appropriated it for the title of his autobiography.[314]

The New Space crowd, particularly Musk, felt different-ly. It is a widely held opinion that as NASA has aged, it has become increasingly risk averse. The agency feared failure in a way that was increasing complexity, driving up costs, and delaying schedules. Perfect had become the enemy of good enough. Nothing could be more emblematic of this than the Space Shuttle program, which, despite a constant focus on safety, killed 4 percent of the astronauts who participated in it.[315] NASA's new rocket, the Space Launch System, would also be designed for perfection. It would be so expensive that it would have to work perfectly the first time; and it did.

Branson is an ardent adventurer and has risked his own life on multiple attempts to set records in boats and balloons.[316] Bezos and Musk came from the internet software world and were used to the iterative development model, where systems were tested, modified, and retested until a workable (not perfect) solution was found, and the product was released. Designers could try crazy new ideas, programmers could quickly code them, and alpha and beta testers would run them. If the beta looked good, firms would release the code to the public and "see what happens." Problems could easily be fixed in code. We've all experienced those new release blues and the inevitable patches that follow. Many New Space pioneers, particularly Musk, felt the iterative development model could be applied in the unforgiving domain of space hardware in order to break the spiral of cost increases and programmatic delays that were holding back the future they envisioned for humankind.

At first, Musk attempted to reach space by buying a spare Russian ICBM. When this approach failed, he dove into rocket development himself, recruiting a team of experts and relentlessly pushing them to move with alacrity. One of his recruits, Gwynne Shotwell, arranged to launch from a little-used American base on Kwajalein Atoll and get a small contract from the Air Force for SpaceX's small Falcon 1 rocket. Musk named his rocket for Han Solo's spaceship in *Star Wars*, his favorite sci-fi franchise. SpaceX also managed to secure $396 million in NASA funding for development of a larger rocket to meet NASA's needs in the post-shuttle period. Two other firms, Orbital Sciences and Rocketplane Kistler, were selected.[317] NASA terminated the Kistler contact when the firm failed to raise sufficient private capital—a wise requirement of the Commercial Orbital Transportation Services (COTS) program.

It was not surprising that the first two Falcon launches failed to reach orbit. No new organization, including many governments, has ever succeeded with their initial launch. However, when the third Falcon failed, the company was on the brink. Musk decided to fund a fourth attempt, which succeeded in reaching orbit in September of 2008.

Following that success, NASA awarded the firm a life-saving $1.6 billion contract to provide twelve resupply missions to the International Space Station.[318] At the same time, Orbital Sciences (now part of Northrop Grumman) received $1.9 billion for eight resupply missions with its Antares rocket and Cygnus spacecraft. Most of the funds invested into the SpaceX Falcon 9 rocket and Dragon capsule would come from private sources. It would be by far the least expensive and most effective space launch program that NASA had ever participated in.[319] Falcon 9 could loft nearly 23,000 kg (50,000 lb) to LEO. Dragon could return 3,000 kg to Earth, a powerful capability that NASA had not originally required in their COTS contract.[320]

It is hard to overstate the value of SpaceX to the US position in space. Without a commercial solution for resupplying the space station, there is a real chance that the ISS would have been abandoned in the mid-2010s as Russia encountered a series of failures with its Progress and Soyuz vehicles. Being dependent on Russian launches during the Russia–Ukraine War would have been more than just uncomfortable for NASA and the US government.

In 2010, the US had been out of the global space launch business for a couple of decades. Russia, China, and Europe were launching commercial satellites for American companies and the rest of the world. By 2016, SpaceX had single-handedly captured the lion's share of the global space launch market for America, creating billions of dollars in US economic activity and tens of thousands of new, high-paying manufacturing jobs. In 2023, SpaceX launched ninety-five successful missions, nearly half of the global total.[321] Many of these launches were in support of SpaceX's Starlink network, which now comprises the majority of active satellites in orbit.

SpaceX's iterative development process significantly increased the performance of the Falcon 9 between its first flight in 2010 and its "Block 5" iteration in 2018, but not without failure. A Falcon 9 upper stage exploded during a flight to the ISS in 2015, and another one blew up on the pad in 2016. This made putting NASA astronauts onto a SpaceX rocket a hard sell to many at NASA, but when competitor Boeing failed to deliver their crew capsule before SpaceX, the agency had little choice. In 2020, SpaceX became the first commercial company to send humans into orbit. For the moment, it was NASA's only way of sending humans into space missions from American soil and quickly became a popular ride for commercial spaceflight participants as well.

In just three years, SpaceX had launched more people into orbit than the government of China had in their twenty-year human spaceflight program.[322] In 2023, the state-owned China Space News reported that Chinese officials felt their program was "obviously lagging behind" SpaceX and suggested the country should feel a "deep sense of crises" over this.[323]

SpaceX's major US competitor in heavy launch, United Launch Alliance, had just three launches in 2023. Its smaller competitor, Rocket Lab, had eight successes and one failure that year. Jeff Bezos's firm, Blue Origin, had not made any orbital launches as of this writing....

SLOW IS SMOOTH AND SMOOTH IS FAST...MAYBE

Despite being from this software pedigree, Bezos took a far more cautious approach to space launch than Musk. Blue Origin's motto is "Gradatim Ferociter," meaning "Step by Step, Ferociously," and its mascot is a tortoise. Bezos's strategy was to beat his competitors' high-speed hares with quiet persistence.[324] His approach to developing a big, reusable orbital rocket, to be called "New Glenn," was methodical and painstakingly slow.

Elon Musk has a well-known habit of setting impossibly ambitious time schedules and failing to meet them. However, his sense of urgency relentlessly drives his workforce. He eventually delivers on most of his audacious promises. At Blue Origin, even the patience of employees was wearing thin after twenty years without an orbital spaceflight. Even the government moved faster than Bezos's tortoise. After a dozen years of development and much criticism, NASA's huge Space Launch System sent an Orion capsule on a perfect flight to the Moon in the fall of 2022.[325]

Something had to get going at Blue Origin, and when Bezos fired CEO Bob Smith in 2023, nearly everyone seemed pleased.[326] There were reports that Blue Origin's headquarters erupted in cheers when the announcement arrived in employees' inboxes.[327]

Blue Origin had delivered on several important fronts. It's powerful methane + LOX, BE-4 engines were successfully tested and a pair of them delivered to United Launch Alliance to power its Vulcan heavy lift rocket. It's hydrogen + LOX, BE-3 motor had successfully powered twenty-five flights on the suborbital New Shepard system, several of them flying high-paying or high-profile passengers to space including *Star Trek*'s Captain Kirk. Blue had wisely sold their first tickets in an auction for $28 million.[328] Rumor has it that other passengers were paying more than $1 million per seat, which is significantly more than Virgin had been capturing.

REUSABILITY AND ECONOMICS

One of the most impressive things about the New Shepard system was that it was fully autonomous and reusable. The space capsule, carrying six passengers, descended on a parachute to land among the sage, not far from its launch pad on Bezos's sixty-five-thousand-acre holding in West Texas. The booster returned precisely to its launch pad and hovered briefly while landing legs unfolded, and it set down gently like a rocket from a 1950s science fiction film. All that was required to go again was a little maintenance and refueling.

New Shepard became the first reusable, vertically landing space rocket in November of 2015.[329] SpaceX landed an orbital class Falcon 9 booster a month later. To be fair, they were both copying work McDonnell Douglas (now Boeing) had done back in the 1990s with a remarkably innovative low-altitude rocket, the Delta Clipper (DC-X).[330] Virgin was also able to land and reuse the SpaceShipTwo spaceplane and White Knight carrier. Their vehicle made a crewed test flight to space in 2018.[331]

There is a general misconception that SpaceX's price advantage is based on the reusability of their rockets. While the firm surely profits from the reuse of their booster stages, they have not yet passed that savings on to their customers in lower launch prices. SpaceX's advertised launch pricing reached $62 million, years before they succeeded in implementing reuse. That price has actually increased since then. If a price war should come, and China has promised one,[332] SpaceX has a very healthy margin to do battle with.

The initial financial advantage that SpaceX brought to the table was in reducing the cost of manufacturing rockets by increasing efficiencies through process and scale. Back in the day, a commercial or governmental customer would go to a rocket manufacturer like Lockheed, Arianespace, or Great Wall Industries and say, "I have this satellite I need to launch," and the company would start the bespoke process of building one of their rockets for that satellite. About eighteen to twenty-four months later, the $200 to $400 million launch vehicle would be ready to fly. When that rocket was done, the company would begin another. Companies like ULA firmly believed there would only be a dozen launches a year, max.[333]

SpaceX upended this and began to manufacture rockets like automobiles, at a continuous rate of production. Metal flowed in one end of the factory, and rockets would flow out of the other, regardless of demand. Musk sought production engineers who had experience in efficient factories, not aerospace ones. This included Vice President of Production Andy Lambert, who had run BMW's UK plant, which built MINI Coopers.[334]

Business development would proceed independently from the manufacturing process. Musk understood that by lowering the cost of production, he could lower his price and improve responsiveness, and sales would follow. Prices did drop, and soon SpaceX launches were so inexpensive that executives at China's state-owned Great Wall Industry Corporation were "confounded" at the ability of an American company to undercut their cheap launches.[335]

There was also disbelief and resistance to this pricing at home. At first, the DoD was not about to trust this disruptive California startup with their "exquisite" space assets. SpaceX sued the Air Force more than once[336] and took the issue to Congress. In testimony to the House Armed Services Committee, SpaceX president Gwynne Shotwell was asked how her firm was able to significantly undercut the prices offered by incumbent United Launch Alliance. She replied, "I don't know how to build a $400 million rocket."[337]

ROCKET LAB, RELATIVITY, AND MORE CROWD THE FIELD

A number of New Space startups have moved from the PowerPoint slide deck to hardware in the last decade. The most successful is Rocket Lab, a New Zealand startup founded by self-taught genius Peter Beck. Beck simplified the design of his kerolox engine by replacing the mechanical fuel pumps with electric ones. This design worked out great for a small rocket named "Electron," which first reached orbit in 2018. The rocket's size makes economies of scale hard to achieve, but its minimalist design makes it easy to transport and prepare for launch. The firm has announced a larger and more reusable methane LOX rocket, the Neutron, which can deliver up to 8,000 kg (15,000 lb) to orbit and compete with the SpaceX Falcon 9 in the launching of satellite constellations.[338] The firm officially relocated its headquarters to the United States in 2013 and now resides in a commercial park adjacent to the Long Beach Airport, which has become a hub for commercial space startups.

Other small launch firms followed, including Firefly, a company founded by former SpaceX and Virgin engineer Tom Markusic in 2014. Firefly was bankrupted by lawsuits over the intellectual property used in the kerolox engines of its Alpha rocket. The firm's assets were bought out by a colorful Ukrainian businessperson, Max Polyakov, and it quickly turned around.[339] Firefly acquired NASA and Air Force contracts and achieved a $1 billion valuation. Some in the US government were uncomfortable with Polyakov's position, and under pressure from the Committee on Foreign Investment in the United States (CFIUS), his firm, Noosphere, sold its holdings in early 2022.[340] The Alpha rocket reached orbit in October of 2022 from Vandenberg Space Force Base. The Space Force has tasked the firm with developing responsive launch capabilities that could be used to replenish US lost satellites quickly in the event of a CME event or ASAT attack.[341]

Not to be left out of the satellite launch business, Richard Branson leveraged his firm's aviation and air launch experience to start a company, Virgin Orbit. The firm successfully launched a small payload into space from under the wing of a former Virgin Atlantic 747 in 2021. Sadly, the firm encountered a perfect financial storm in 2023. Branson's travel-dependent Virgin empire had suffered enormously during COVID, interest rates were up, and the "Special Purpose Acquisition Company" (SPAC) mechanism the firm had used to raise public funds lost its luster on Wall Street. A launch failure shook investor confidence, and the firm was quickly moved into bankruptcy.[342] Virgin Orbit's facility was directly adjacent to Rocket Lab's in Long Beach, and Peter Beck scooped up the facility and most of the physical assets. Beck invited his employees to explore the Virgin factory, which he felt had been overequipped and overstocked, and reportedly told them, "This is what failure looks like."[343]

From 2009 to 2023, the United States went from having a single space launch company to a half-dozen credible ones, with literally dozens of startups in the wings. Success in such a crowded field requires a sustainable competitive advantage. Two students from the University of Southern California, Tim Ellis and Jordan Noone, found a relative advantage in additive manufacturing. The startup they founded, Relativity Space, 3D prints almost everything in their methane + LOX-powered orbital rocket. This unique capability appealed to investors who appreciated the cost and speed advantage it afforded in rocket production and the applications that large-scale metal printing might bring to other industries. Relativity has raised more than $1.5 billion.[344] They are headquartered in Long Beach, California, and have a large test and manufacturing site at NASA's Stennis Space Center in Mississippi. Their Terran rockets will fly from dedicated launch pads at Cape Canaveral and at Vandenberg.[345]

A PLETHORA OF SPACEPORTS

All of these cool new rockets need somewhere to fly from. Below is a list of US launch facilities that have hosted successful orbital launches:

> **Cape Canaveral Space Force Station, Kennedy Space Center, and Space Florida Launch Complex** support military, civil, and commercial launches from Merritt Island on Central Florida's east coast.

Space launches occur almost weekly from the many launch pads at these three closely coordinated facilities. SpaceX, ULA, Blue Origin, Relativity, and many others launch or test from here.

Vandenberg Space Force Base in central California provides access to polar orbits for primarily military and increasingly commercial launches. ULA, SpaceX, Firefly, and Relativity have pads here.

The Pacific Spaceport Complex on Kodiak Island, Alaska, provides polar launches for mainly newer and smaller rockets. It is a popular place to test less proven systems. Astra, ABL, and other small launch firms have favored this location.

The Mid-Atlantic Regional Spaceport (MARS) at Wallops Island, Virginia, provides eastbound equatorial and inclined launches for NASA and commercial firms. Rocket Lab and Orbital ATK/Northrop Grumman utilize this facility.

The Mojave Air and Space Port in California's High Desert supported orbital space launches by Virgin Orbit as well as suborbital spaceflights by Scaled Composites and Virgin.

The Ronald Reagan Ballistic Missile Defense Test Site on Kwajalein Atoll in the Marshall Islands supported orbital space launches by Orbital's Pegasus air launch system as well as SpaceX's Falcon 1.

Several other aspiring spaceports have received licenses, primarily for suborbital and horizontal launch activities.[346] These include Spaceport America near Truth or Consequences, New Mexico, which is home to Virgin Galactic's spaceflight operations. Spaceport Camden on Georgia's east coast was granted an FAA license but lacks a tenant with a working rocket.

As every rocket has unique launch towers and supporting infrastructure, they need dedicated pads. The limited available pads in Florida are running out. The Space Force has been looking for operational and business models that will allow for multi-tenant pads. Executive students at Arizona State University's Thunderbird School of Global Management produced a report for the Space Force in 2022 that noted, "The leadership of the United States can be secured by increased investment and transformation of the domestic launch architecture" and proposed that revenue bonds be issued to support the development of a working multi-tenant spaceport in Florida.[347]

Another solution for overcrowding on the coast is to move launches offshore. In the late 1990s, a multinational company, Sea Launch, provided orbital launch services from a refitted mobile oil rig named Odyssey and a support vessel called the *Sea Launch Commander*. Both ships docked in California's Long Beach harbor, and the firm utilized Russian-built Zenit rockets. Competition from SpaceX and deteriorating US–Russian relations resulted in the failure of the company. Naturally, China tried to buy the firm's assets.[348] They were not able to but duplicated the technology, and China National Space Administration (CNSA) began launching rockets from sea in 2022.[349] A nominally commercial Chinese firm followed the next year.[350]

A new attempt at this model, supporting American-built rockets, is emerging today. The Spaceport Company has a mobile, offshore platform capable of launching small rockets like the Firefly Alpha rockets off the coast of Florida or Texas.[351] Operating just off Cape Canaveral could allow the firm to leverage the airspace protection and tracking capabilities of the Space Force and NASA facilities.

THE EMPIRE STRIKES BACK

With the Space Shuttle proving to be an unreliable launch solution, the USAF created the Evolved Expendable Launch Vehicle, or EELV, program to support launches by traditional rockets; specifically, Boeing's Delta II and Lockheed's Atlas V. Following the collapse of Teledesic and the bankruptcy of Iridium, the launch providers viewed competing for a shrinking number of commercial launches against heavily subsidized state-owned enterprises from China, Russia, and Europe as extremely unattractive. The Air Force made sure to give both firms launches in order to keep them in the game and assure that the military and intelligence services had redundant access to space.[352] When Boeing executives were caught stealing Lockheed Martin bid documents,[353] the government pressured the two firms to merge their operations and keep both rockets flying. United Launch Alliance was born in 2005 as a fifty-fifty joint venture between the two aerospace giants. It was this monopoly market that SpaceX began to aggressively disrupt with lower prices and legal challenges.

Seeing the SpaceX writing on the wall, ULA's parents wisely recruited a brilliant, innovative, and outgoing engineer to lead the enterprise. Salvatore "Tory" Bruno faced the unenviable task of facing off with tenacious and mercurial Musk while reporting to parents who did not always get along. The evenly split ownership meant that either Boeing or Lockheed Martin could shut down any initiative they didn't care for, but nobody could force anything forward.

As if that were not enough, the firm's workhorse, the Atlas V, faced an existential challenge. "Mighty Atlas" had been designed around powerful and reliable RD-180 rocket engines produced in Russia.[354] As relations with that country declined, pressure built on the firm to replace the engines. There weren't many practical engine options in the US, other than those from Aerojet Rocketdyne already being used in the Delta line. They were very expensive and used hydrogen, a powerful but difficult to handle fuel. Bruno made the bold decision to replace the Atlas with a new rocket, the Vulcan, and to purchase new BE-4 methalox engines from Blue Origin. The rocket's Centaur high-energy upper stage would keep the venerable Aerojet RL10 engines. The dependency on Bezos's slow-moving tortoise delayed the Vulcan significantly[355] and resulted in SpaceX grabbing almost all of the launch opportunities in 2023. Vulcan successfully launched a commercial payload toward the Moon in January of 2024.[i] The big ULA rocket is particularly adept at delivering large payloads to higher orbits and can loft 15,000 kg (33,700 lb) to a geostationary transfer orbit,[356] nearly twice the Falcon 9's 8,300 kg (18,000 lb).[357]

ULA also envisioned an alternative approach to reusability. Bruno argued that almost all of the value in a rocket was

---

i   Although the Vulcan rocket performed flawlessly, the Peregrine lander suffered a serious technical malfunction and failed to land on the Moon.

concentrated in the engines and the avionics. The big propellant tanks and thin skin that wrapped them were of little value. Landing an entire booster, as SpaceX did, required a great deal of fuel. Reuse consumed 10 percent or more of the booster's performance, which is why the Hawthorne firm offers customers a higher-performance, higher-priced expendable option. Bruno proposed that future versions of the Vulcan could exhaust all propellants and eject the engine package from the rocket. A controllable paraglider would slow the package's descent, and a helicopter would catch it in air.[358] With higher performance, 90 percent of the reusability benefit in hand, and no landing pad or landing barge costs, ULA might just beat SpaceX at the reuse game.

In 2023, it became apparent that Boeing intended to divest itself from ULA and that the rocket company would be sold. Bezos's company, Blue Origin, and private equity firm Cerberus were the two candidates at the time of this writing. Bruno reports that his company has sold seventy Vulcan launches, and many of them are for Bezos's Kuiper project.[359]

MOORE'S LAW OF SPACE AND THE SEARCH FOR THE KILLER APP

The technological improvements in the manufacturing of rockets, the operational economics of reusability, and an increasingly competitive market are driving down the price of space launch, while performance increases. This presents a unique circumstance similar to the one that Moore's Law brought to the computer market. With the price of sending a kilogram of satellite to space moving from more than $50,000 to less than $5,000 over the last few decades, the opportunities for new players to test new ideas in space may mirror the software boom that followed the introduction of the microcomputer.

The CubeSat is a standardized ten-by-ten-centimeter form factor for small satellites developed at California Polytechnic University, San Luis Obispo (Cal Poly SLO). These cubical satellites may be extended from one unit, or 1U, to 3U, 6U, or even 12U configurations. Standards for power, connections, and communications have developed that allow nearly anyone to order parts online and build a working satellite that can be launched on a "rideshare" rocket for a few thousand dollars. Space launches may include more than a hundred of these satellites.[360] NASA's Artemis 1 mission carried a few to the Moon.[361] Imagine a world where disruptive college dropouts can test their wildest ideas in space!

AND THEN THERE'S STARSHIP

Not to take the ULA Vulcan or any threat laying down, Musk has gone all out in pushing the advantages that Tsiolkovsky's rocket equation offers to bigger rockets. His new Starship spacecraft and Super Heavy booster promise to revolutionize spaceflight the way that Apple's Macintosh computer and iPhones changed their respective markets. Starship is huge, powerful, and extremely reusable. It's the biggest, baddest rocket ever built by any metric. It can deliver 150 metric tons (330,000 lb) to orbit in reusable mode or an astounding 250 metric tons (550,000 lb) in an expendable (non-recovered) launch. That's ten times more than the original Falcon 9. Starship's expected levels of reusability promise us the few hundreds of dollars per pound to orbit that the Space Shuttle was supposed to deliver. If it works, the possibility space of those killer space apps will have just grown by an order of magnitude.

Perhaps more importantly, Starship should also provide a large downmass, allowing it to potentially function as a high-volume orbital factory with its own return capability. We've not seen numbers on Starship's Earth downmass, though it is reasonable to assume that it should be able to return more material than anything that has gone before. NASA has contracted with SpaceX to use a variant of the Starship upper stage as a lunar lander, and that is expected to deliver a crew and one hundred metric tons of supplies to the lunar surface.[362]

When Musk first revealed the Starship at a conference in Guadalajara, Mexico, he named it "BFR," which apparently stood for "Big F***king Rocket," and suggested that it would carry "at least a hundred people" to Mars, per flight. Starship uses methalox engines for both stages, reflecting Musk's interest in Mars as a destination. CO_2 in the Martian atmosphere can be combined with hydrogen from water to produce methane.[ii]

As of this writing, Starship has had three test launches from Starbase, SpaceX's private launch facility at Boca Chica, Texas. The first two failed to reach their intended altitude and final destinations, but both were declared a success by Musk and the firm's supporters who witnessed the demonstration of Raptor engines lifting something this huge to the edge of space to be proof of great things to come. In the third test

---

ii   ULA and Blue Origin have both chosen methalox for their boosters but hydrogen for their upper stages, which better supports a lunar economy based on water ice.

flight, on March 14, 2024, the Super Heavy booster lofted the Starship into space. The massive spacecraft successfully separated, tested its payload bay doors and performed a transfer of propellants test. It later reentered over its intended target zone over the Indian Ocean. China appears to have a very long way to go to catch up with Starship, though they are already on that path. In an April 2021 presentation, a Chinese state-owned firm showed a video highlighting their latest "innovation," which was a computer-generated image showing a nearly exact copy of Starship.[363]

LESSONS LEARNED: KEEP MOVING FORWARD WITH PRIVATE ENTERPRISE OUT IN FRONT

America cannot afford to be risk averse at this juncture. Continued support for innovative and risky projects like Vulcan's unique engine recovery program, Relativity's 3D-printed rockets, and Musk's Starship are the path forward for beating China.

We must ignore the naysayers and backbiters who will always argue that now (with a laundry list of crises) is not the time for any bold action. They fear ambition and disdain success. No nation who listened to doomsayers has ever prospered.

China is intimidated by the efficiency of American private space enterprises. As Xi cracks down on private markets and independent thought, America must reembrace those strengths in space. History has shown that China will copy everything America does, and we must be relentless innovators to prosper.

Failure does not mean lost assets or employees. When Virgin Orbit failed, its assets simply moved to Rocket Lab, and its talented employees moved to other aerospace firms. While the investors lost money, the United States did not.

Bigger is better in space. Getting more mass and more people into space, to the Moon, and back to Earth will give America the advantage in development of and production in space that will boost our economy far beyond China's challenge. Vulcan, New Glenn, SLS, and Starship are leading the way.

CHAPTER ONE

DEFENDING AND DEFINING THE FUTURE: SPACE FORCE, ARTEMIS, REGULATION, AND GEOPOLITICS

On accessible terrain,
He who occupies high Yang ground
And ensures his line of supplies
Will fight to advantage.
On precipitous terrain,
If we occupy it first,
We should hold the Yang heights
and wait for the enemy.
If the enemy occupies it first, do not go after him,
But entice him out by retreating.
—Sun Tzu[364]

It is clear that absent a geopolitical motivation, governmental interest in space wanes. Competition is a powerful motivator. It got NASA from zero to 238,855 miles—the distance to the Moon—in just eight short years! Cooperation has resulted in stagnation. In the five decades since the celebrated 1975 "handshake in space" between astronauts and cosmonauts, nobody traveled more than 350 miles from Earth. Cold War 2.0, new technologies, and bold entrepreneurs are changing that.

COMPETITION IS A MOTIVATOR; THE THREAT OF CONFLICT IS AN EVEN STRONGER ONE

As we've documented in this book, space is simultaneously a land of promise and plenty and strategic military high ground. Spaceflight has been militarized since German rockets brought us into the Space Age. Russia and China always have and will continue to keep their civil and commercial space entities tightly bound to their armed forces.

President Trump created the United States Space Force in 2019 with the goal of enhancing America's preeminent position in space-based defense capabilities. This plan received bipartisan support in Congress. The Space Force does not, initially, create any additional capabilities—nobody is building a Death Star or cloning an army of stormtroopers—it consolidates activities that were already occurring. Before the USSF was formed, America's space capabilities were dominated by the Air Force but loosely coordinated, often across service branches. The leadership of the Air Force is always in the hands of former fighter jocks. Nobody from Space Command or Space Systems Command was going to get to the top. Consequently, with a lack of space savvy in top leadership, the Air Force's notoriously mismanaged acquisition system always supports bloated airplane programs. When they thought of space, they viewed it primarily as a tool for enhancing air superiority and supporting terrestrial warfighters on land and at sea. Space capabilities for *use in space* make little sense to the Air Force brass. The idea that we will soon be needing to defend commercial actors on the Moon is completely lost on them. It's like trying to explain the value of an aircraft carrier to WWI gunboat admirals fixated on building battleships.

THE OUTER SPACE TREATY

In 1967, the United States signed the Treaty on Principles Governing the Activities of States in the Exploration and Use of Outer Space, including the Moon and Other Celestial Bodies, also known as the Outer Space Treaty (OST).[365] One hundred fourteen nations, including every real space power, signed this agreement, which forms the basis for international space law and drives US domestic law and regulations.

The OST's best point is its prohibition, under Article IV, of placing nuclear weapons or "any other kinds of weapons of mass destruction" in space. This was a dinkum agreement with the Soviet Union. When the Soviets put a cannon on Salyut-3, they were not violating the treaty, and the US could be fairly certain that Russians were transactional enough not to violate the OST. The problem with China is their clear history of ignoring the agreements they've signed onto, as well as international norms of behavior, while pretending that they are the very model of global civil citizens. This is an unstated but major reason why there has been so little effort to bring China into a nuclear arms agreement. What would be the point? As China lofts more and bigger things into to space, it is going to be hard to tell if Article IV simply ties America's hands behind its back.

Other provisions of the OST are outright troubling for the American way of thinking. When the treaty was signed, America was running that "we can do communism better than the Soviets" centralized government space program. Only crazy people were thinking about an entrepreneurial future of commerce in space. Consequently, the OST reads like an agreement between authoritarian socialist states. Everything in it is state-focused, and there are no specific references to commercial activities or actors.

What we do have is Article II, which prohibits national appropriation and sovereignty on the Moon and elsewhere in space. Without national sovereignty, it is hard to image how the rule of law, so essential to investment and commerce, can exist. There is no provision for ownership or demarcation of private property or any process for staking claims over natural resources. There are no clear paths for adjudication of disputes between private parties or any enforcement mechanisms. Those concepts require governmental authority over territory, i.e., "sovereignty," and in the absence of that, what do we have? A United Nations committee? It is difficult to believe that an American company developing a Mars colony would get a fair or timely hearing at the UN. The CCP has developed expertise at co-opting multilateral organizations via pressure and bribery directed at the constituent members.

Article VI is also important. It asserts that states that are signatories to the OST are financially responsible for "national activities in outer space" including by "non-governmental entities." This provision essentially makes the US government the liability insurer of last resort for any and all commercial action in space. Article VI results in the need for careful regulation of private activities to minimize governmental risk.

The US government takes their liability in the area of launch and reentry very seriously. The FAA's Office of Commercial Space Transportation (FAA/AST) has the authority to issue licenses and permits for space vehicles and spaceports conducting these operations. The office has a perfect record in this regard. All of our rockets are required to deposit their stages into the ocean or recover them in a controlled manner. No person or property has been injured or damaged by a misguided US commercial space vehicle.

CCP DON'T CARE

Not everyone takes their Article VI responsibilities as seriously as the US's FAA does. *The New York Times* described China's handling of a Long March 5B rocket core following a launch in 2022:

> It was China's latest round of celestial roulette involving a deliberate uncontrolled atmospheric re-entry. The rocket stage, by design, did not include a system to guide it into a specific spot on Earth, far away from people. [366]

Theoretically, when one of these twenty-three-ton rocket cores crashes into a city, Xi Jinping will write the survivors a check, though we are still waiting on our COVID reparations.

Speaking of Chinese rocket crashes, let us tell you about a doozy and how it sparked the creation of some very contentious US space regulations. On February 15, 1996, an American communications satellite built by Space Systems/Loral was launched from China's Xichang Satellite Launch Center. *Smithsonian Magazine* published an excerpt from the diary of a US engineer near the launch site:

Instead of rising vertically for nine seconds and several thousand feet I saw it traveling horizontally, accelerating as it progressed down the valley, only a few hundred feet off the ground.... And our next reaction was Holy shit, we need to get off the roof.... I knew what was coming, but the instant of horror that is burned into memory was not anticipated. A tremendous light turned 3 a.m. into noon. Every tree on the hillside was clear as a knife edge, and the sky reflected a weird glow, a color I cannot describe.... Many things happened at once. I heard the biggest explosion of my life, I turned and started to run. I saw a friend's face contorted in Oh shit! I heard a smaller and then a larger boom, I left the ground, I was on the ground, scrambling, wondering why I was down there.... I heard glass breaking and shit was flying everywhere.[367]

The Americans survived, but the rocket had slammed directly into a village, destroying dozens of buildings. The explosion likely killed over a hundred innocent people.[i] This was not the first time. The horrific failure of Long March 2E carrying a Hughes satellite, just a year earlier, had already prompted a ban on viewing launches from nearby rooftops.

When the remains of the Loral satellite were recovered, the sensitive encryption technology was found to be missing.

i   The usual CCP cover-up operation made it impossible to determine the exact death count, but reports by Americans on-site and videos of the decimated village make it clear it was a major disaster.

Subsequent congressional investigations and statements from those present revealed a consistent pattern of Chinese espionage and a lax attitude on the part of the American personnel throughout the entire operation. Worse, Loral and Hughes addressed the problem by helping the Chinese improve their launch guidance technology, a bonehead move that clearly had dual-use applications for ICBMs.[368]

Following a congressional investigation, the firms involved were fined, and US satellite technology was added to the United States Munitions List (USML) and placed under the regulatory regime known as the International Traffic in Arms Regulations (ITAR). The upside to this was that no American satellites would ever be launched by Chinese rockets.

The downside was that, lacking any competitive domestic launch options, the American satellite building industry and most of its supply chain quickly collapsed. According to the UN's Office of Outer Space Affairs, the United States accounted for more than half of global satellite registrations in 1997 (eighty-eight of 152) and less than a fourth by 2008 (twenty-four of 109).[369] This heavy-handed and non-strategic approach has been extremely unpopular in the commercial space sector.[370] On the other hand, it also spurred demand for domestic launch capabilities, providing work for SpaceX and Rocket Lab. America regained a satellite majority by 2017 (286 of 456).

OUR REGULATORS HAVE A TOUGH JOB JUST KEEPING UP

While the FAA has kept America safe, it has been challenged in keeping up with the exponentially increasing demand for space launch and reentry licensing. Industry has grumbled about the general delays and encouraged the agency to increase staffing.[371] The FAA has been moving as quickly as a government agency can, but there are simply not a lot of space launch and reentry experts looking for government jobs.[372] The situation has produced a couple of cases of notable concern.

Varda is a Southern California producer of orbital space manufacturing laboratories with downmass capabilities built in. If you make stuff in space to benefit Earth, you're going to need to bring it back. Varda launched their first capsule in June of 2023 and completed a microgravity experiment to grow pharmaceutical crystals that could aid in the treatment of HIV. The FAA denied the firm a reentry license that would allow it to bring those samples back and to demonstrate their ability to reenter and land in the Utah desert. Coordination with the US military wasn't going well either.[373] The FAA position appeared to punish Varda because the firm didn't do their paperwork in the proper order. It appears that Varda grabbed a launch opportunity on a SpaceX rideshare mission before completing their reentry licensing, which may have been delayed by the FAA's own backlog. The company moved their reentry to Australia, which appeared to be more accommodating.[374] On February 14, the FAA responded at the last minute with a reentry license, and the firm successfully deorbited their capsule on February 21.[375]

Another case that has attracted a great deal of attention has been the test launches of SpaceX's massive Starship rocket. The Starbase launch facility is far south, faces eastward, and the area is remote and sparsely populated. It's an attractive and safe site for space launches. The world's richest man can never catch a break, however, and there were inevitably a lot of complaints about the operation. When SpaceX submitted its launch application, the FAA received eighteen thousand public comments[376] on the environmental impact. Respondents worried about everything from bird reproduction to Civil War artifacts.[377] Processing these consumed resources, money, and time. Opponents of progress understand they can "paper" a project to death in America, but regulatory delays and public concerns will not delay China's Starship clone.

Luckily, FAA/AST's mandate is not to simply regulate space companies but also to "encourage, facilitate, and promote" the commercial space industry.[378] Its sister office in the Department of Commerce, the Office of Space Commerce, was formed at the same time and defines its mission as: "to foster the conditions for the economic growth and technological advancement of the U.S. commercial space industry."[379]

Getting back to the Article VI liability situation, things become more complicated when you consider thousands of satellites. If two satellites bump into each other, who is responsible? China complained about a Starlink satellite getting too close to their Tiangong space station, despite the fact that the Starlink satellite was in its orbit before the Chinese launched their space station.[380]

What about multinational corporations or non-state actors? Imagine if a hypothetical wayward satellite belonging to Apple were to collide with a Russian Soyuz craft, and the crew died. Would the US taxpayer be responsible? Note, this is the same Apple that kept an international headquarters in Ireland's tax haven to avoid paying billions of dollars of US corporate income taxes[381] and mostly employs people in China. What if they bought that satellite from a Japanese company and launched it on a European rocket? Do you want to foot that bill?

Theoretically, when two commercial rovers bump noses on the unregulated (Article II's ban on sovereignty) surface of the Moon, the bill for that lunar fender bender may have to be argued by the Department of State at the United Nations and paid for by a government. Imagine an O'Neillian future with "millions of people living and working in space." What if some of them assert they are not subject to the jurisdiction of any earthly state? At some point in our sci-fi future, the OST's state liability plus no sovereignty model must totally fail.

WHAT ABOUT THAT SPACE JUNK?

One of the key regulatory questions is what to do about that space debris that everyone loves to talk about but that few people actually understand. Firstly, it is important to note that as with most crises, the space debris problem is nowhere near as bad as it is made out to be. Secondly, most of the uncontrolled space junk was created by governmental programs, and much of the worst stuff is the result of the messy ASAT test conducted by China and Russia.

Space debris can be solved by doing three simple things and working on one hard thing.

1. Don't do any destructive ASAT testing.
2. Provide accurate and timely data to everyone on the location of space assets aka space situational awareness.
3. License orbital positions in advance and require all rocket stages and satellites to be controllable and deorbit safely when they are no longer in use aka space traffic management.
4. Remove dangerous debris from orbit. (The hard thing.)

The US has the first three of these under control. The DoD provides accurate data to the world on the location of tens of thousands of space objects. The FCC has unilaterally taken it upon themselves to manage deorbit requirements. However, the Trump administration's Space Policy Directive-3 (SPD-3) designated the Office of Space Commerce to provide a unified solution for space debris.[382] The Biden White House has supported that directive, but Congress has failed to provide legislation and funding necessary for its full enactment. We offer a proposal for the fourth point in our final chapter.

ARTEMIS

After decades stuck in LEO, the threat of competition with China for influence and economic development on the Moon has awoken our spirit of exploration and shifted American space policy out of low Earth orbit. President Trump was probably the first American president to clearly understand the nature of China as a rapacious global competitor, and we were proud to be part of the team that advised him to return America to the Moon, where China is clearly aiming to secure strategic resources. NASA's Artemis Moon program has received bipartisan support, and if all goes well, the Artemis 2 mission will carry Americans back to lunar space by 2025.

Most importantly, President Trump's Space Policy Directive-1 (SPD-1) modified the Obama-era directive to include:

> Lead an innovative and sustainable program of exploration with commercial and international partners to enable human expansion across the solar system and to bring back to Earth new knowledge and opportunities.

Beginning with missions beyond low-Earth orbit, the United States will lead the return of humans to the Moon for long-term exploration and utilization, followed by human missions to Mars and other destinations.

The important words here are "sustainable," "long-term," and "utilization." We are not doing "Flags and Footprints" again. We are returning to the Moon long-term to utilize the resources there and to build a sustainable space economy centered around commercial activities. The goal is very clear: America intends to lead humanity in settling the solar system and in improving life on Earth with the riches found there. We will not leave the future of humanity in space or on our home planet to be defined by China and Russia.

The major components of the Artemis lunar program include the Orion capsule started under the Bush administration's Constellation Program and the Space Launch System, which is a reworked version of the Ares V rocket. The SLS uses the powerful RS-25 engines left over from the Space Shuttle orbiters, but it is not reusable. There has been criticism over the cost effectiveness of those design choices, but the rocket works great. An Orion capsule circled the Moon and returned to Earth in 2022. The Artemis 2 rocket and capsule are in final preparation. Like Apollo 8, the crew will not land but will circle the Moon and test systems for the landing mission.

The Artemis 3 mission was originally planned to land humans near the lunar south pole in 2025. The landing will use a modified version of the SpaceX Starship spacecraft called the Human Landing System (HLS), which may not be ready by that time. The Government Accountability Office (GAO) has suggested that the reality of building a crewed lunar lander will likely push the Artemis landing out to 2027.[383] SpaceX has noted that delays in licensing its Starship tests from Boca Chica are not helping the schedule. If the lander is late, it is likely that the Artemis 3 mission will dock with the planned Gateway station in a special orbit around L2. Future missions may depart for the lunar surface via the Gateway. A second HLS contract has been awarded to Blue Origin to "increase competition, reduce costs to taxpayers, support a regular cadence of lunar landings, further invest in the lunar economy."[384]

THE ARTEMIS ACCORDS

SPD-1 requires the exploration program to be international. Working with the Department of State, NASA has signed more than thirty nations onto the Artemis Accords, a set of operating principles that provide for mutual cooperation and assistance while developing the Moon.[385] The accords internationalize a critical capitalistic principal that is already enshrined in domestic US law. The Commercial Space Launch Competitiveness Act of 2015 specifically allows US citizens and companies to engage in "the commercial exploration and exploitation of space resources." Section 10 of the Artemis Accords states, "The Signatories affirm that the extraction of space resources does not inherently constitute national appropriation under Article II of the Outer Space Treaty."[386]

NO BUCKS, NO BUCK ROGERS

All this Moon stuff sounds expensive, but is it? While NASA's programs are very popular and highly visible, we really don't spend much on our space agency. In 2022, the US Treasury took in revenues of $4.9 trillion and then charged up another $1.4 trillion so the federal government could spend a whopping $6.3 trillion. Of that largesse, NASA received a historically generous appropriation of $24 billion. Still, that was just 0.35 percent of federal spending. Because our government is growing faster than our economy—creating inflation in the process—this increase was actually a drop relative to NASA's portion of the budget in the previous year. Congress could axe the entire NASA budget, and the "savings" would be utterly invisible on a graph of federal spending.[387]

Let us wrap up with some frightening budgetary context. The GAO reports that the Air Force's $1.7 trillion F-35 program is $165 billion over budget.[388] You could fit three years of the entire NASA and DoD space budget into just the overrun on that single Air Force boondoggle. The United States spent $905 billion on Medicare in 2022. Annual GAO reports typically find about $50 billion of these expenditures were used to pay fraudulent claims. If you aren't a fan of how efficient a particular NASA program is, please remember that Congress knowingly hands twice the NASA budget to medical criminals each and every year.[389] Also recall what you've learned here about the past, current, and future returns on our investment in space. America can afford to have a future.

LESSONS LEARNED: YOU GOTTA SPEND MONEY TO MAKE MONEY AND PLAY WELL WITH OTHERS

International competition and even the threat of looming conflict can be strong motivators for constructive action. President Trump embraced Space Race 2.0, determined to see America go further and achieve more.

International agreements that appeared to make sense to our grandfathers may require reinterpretation for today's realities, including the OST in light of space commercialization and China's lack of regard for its treaty obligations and for international norms.

Weakness invites aggression. The White House and Congress have supported increased Space Force budgets to ensure we stay ahead of China in this critical area and avoid conflict by maintaining overwhelming superiority.

The US has successfully engaged the world in support of America's vision of returning to the Moon and developing resources. This has overwhelmed the Russia–China lunar alliance.

LIFTOFF

AMERICA MUST GO!

The desire for safety stands against every great and noble enterprise.
—Tacitus[390]

The United States now sits astride the global space business in much the way that it dominated so many industries of the last century. America is launching most of the world's rockets. America is building most of the world's satellites. Foreign startups don't just set up design studios in California, they move their headquarters there, build real factories, and conduct their operations in the United States. Space entrepreneurs are immigrating to America, and global investors are pouring capital into US space startups. In what other manufacturing industry is that true? Our policy makers and regulators deserve a round of applause for creating an attractive business environment while successfully protecting our national security and ensuring public safety.

We are also the world's explorers, drawing the maps and breaking our own records. NASA has far more satellites orbiting our planet than any other nation's space agency. We fly more astronauts than anyone else. We are the only country to have robotically explored all the planets in our solar system (including Ceres and Pluto[i]). We walked on the Moon, and we are going back to develop it.

Our military capabilities in space are peerless. America has redundant and responsive access to space, the best in-space maneuverability, and the ability to deny those capabilities to others. The space industrial base supporting that strength is by far the best in the world.

America could just do a mic drop here, but history shows that being number one is transitory, and our competitors in Communist China are students of history. We must keep our sleeves rolled up and stay at work. Here is a partial list of what must be done soon:

BEAT CHINA TO THE MOON

While NASA originally targeted "Boots on the Moon" for 2024, that date slipped to 2025 and now looks like 2027. Meanwhile, Communist China has announced a 2030 Moon landing, and they have been relentlessly on time in other space endeavors. There will be no silver medal. If the Chinese sink their flag first, is Congress going to spend billions so America can be runner-up?

---

i   Pluto, the only planet discovered by an American, was demoted by astronomers meeting in Paris based on its orbit crossing Neptune's. It wasn't entirely clear why Neptune wasn't similarly demoted, other than that it was discovered by a German. Planetary scientists, who study the actual nature of planets rather than their orbits, are generally in agreement that Pluto is a planet and that there are likely dozens of planets in our solar system.

The crucial item in this race is the Human Landing System. Both of the HLS designs NASA is supporting depend on on-orbit cryogenic refueling, an important capability that has never been demonstrated before. Pressure must be kept on SpaceX and Blue Origin to deliver. They also need extraordinary support. In particular, we must clear licensing backlogs, smooth regulations, and remove perfunctory legal hurdles that slow testing.

STAY ON THE MOON

Beating China is not enough. China, Russia, and a collection of dubious allies are building a Moon base. We must remain committed to the mandate in President Trump's first Space Policy Directive for a sustained and permanent human presence on the Moon. Language from NASA has wavered on this point. Our commitment to stay on the Moon must be unambiguous.

DEVELOP THE MOON FOR THE BENEFIT OF THE US AND FREE WORLD

Funding from the US Geographical Survey (USGS) should be provided for research and development of dual-use mining technologies that enable both space resource extraction and advanced terrestrial mining. Some specific technologies include the rapid detection and automated assaying of subsurface mineral deposits and AI-enabled autonomous deep mining systems. NASA's Science Mission Directorate should be funded to conduct additional exploration of lunar and asteroid resources.

SUPPORT AND ENABLE COMMERCIAL DEVELOPMENT OF MARS

Mars is an expensive and distant mission for NASA. Today's goal must be beating China in securing the resources of cis-lunar space. Brilliant minds like Elon Musk of SpaceX and Tim Ellis of Relativity Space are eager to support commercial development of Mars with private capital. The US government must be there to facilitate those efforts and broadly engage the power of entrepreneurs and private investors in meeting national space goals, much as the British Empire supported private overseas development via commercial ventures such as the East India Company.

EDUCATE, EDUCATE, EDUCATE

Aerospace engineering, space business, space law, and space policy programs should be supported.

FREE THE PRIVATE SECTOR AND ENSURE OUR REGULATIONS ARE ALIGNED TO WIN

Winning the second space race is all about the private sector. We won't beat China in a competition of large governmental programs; commercial space is America's best weapon. Continued engagement of the commercial space sector is critical, and retaining the world's factory floor for space is a prerequisite for success in science, exploration, and military space. President Trump's second Space Policy Directive called for streamlining regulations to "minimize uncertainty for taxpayers, investors, and private industry." This policy directive should guide legislation and regulatory behavior.

The offices supporting the commercial sector must be in positions of consequence appropriate to the significance of this industry and their mandates. The Office of Space Commerce must be removed from inside of NOAA and restored to its original position within the department, reporting directly to the Secretary of Commerce. The Office of Commercial Space Transportation must similarly be removed from under the FAA and restored to its original position, reporting to the Secretary of Transportation. This office should also be directed by a presidential appointee.

DEAL WITH THE DEBRIS

Everyone agrees that keeping space accessible and low Earth orbit safe is critical. The mandate in President Trump's third Space Policy Directive must be implemented, and the Office of Space Commerce must be adequately funded to fulfill that important function.

Rather than funding an expensive governmental system for debris removal, governments responsible for creating the debris (China, Russia, the US, and Europe) should establish a fund and pay a bounty to any organization, governmental or commercial, that removes their debris. Objects could be valued based on their nature, size, and orbit. The most dangerous ones will be tagged with the highest bounty. This debris bounty system will engage global private capital and produce competitive solutions with multiple future applications. Most importantly, nothing is paid out until debris is actually cleared. We do recognize the reality that China and Russia are unlikely to be cooperative and that Europe will write a very tiny check. America will once again have to take the lead here and likely foot the bill, but we also have the most to gain as our commercial firms dominate LEO.

CLARIFY ROLES

The FCC must be entirely focused on its job of allocating and protecting the radio spectrum. The Office of Commercial Space Transportation must remain wholly dedicated to the task of streamlining and accelerating the review processes for launch and reentry systems and spaceports. The Office of Space Commerce should handle matters on orbit.

THE SPACE FORCE MUST OWN SPACE

It is time for the Space Force to boldly assume a future-forward role of protecting US governmental and commercial interests in an increasingly congested and conflicted cis-lunar space. That mandate should be clarified, and the Space Force should be transitioned out of the Air Force as a fully independent branch of the military.

CLARIFY OR RENEGOTIATE THE OUTER SPACE TREATY FOR THE TWENTY-FIRST CENTURY

Developing the nearly infinite resources of our solar system for the benefit of all humankind requires that firms are able to compete under free market rules. Congress should be asked to develop follow-up legislation to the Commercial Space Launch Competitiveness Act (CSLCA) of 2015 and work with our partners in the Artemis Accords to include language that supports transferable and collateralizable real property rights for facilities on the Moon, at asteroids, and in desirable orbits.

The lack of sovereignty in Article II impedes enforcement and invites conflict on celestial bodies. Protection under the rule of law must eventually be as clear for individuals and organizations acting in space as it is on Earth. Unpoliced frontiers have a notorious history of conflict and human rights abuses. History on Earth clearly shows that regardless of the treaty language, the CCP will usurp territory on the Moon and implement their draconian rule under de facto sovereignty.

The scope of liability in Article VI must be more clearly defined and constrained so that every action of any entity in a very busy future space environment need not be elevated to the level of state diplomacy.

GO NUCLEAR

Nuclear power is necessary for the development of the Moon and the exploration of deep space. Developing nuclear power technologies for space will benefit Earth, where nuclear offers the only real solution to our longtime environmental concerns. Nuclear propulsion is a well-understood technology that will dramatically shorten trips to Mars, the asteroids, and beyond. It is essential for the development of a space economy.

Additional funding should be provided to the Department of Energy and NASA's Space Technology Mission Directorate for the development of practical nuclear space propulsion and power solutions.

GO SPACE SOLAR

In the future, space-based solar (SBSP) promises to unlock the nearly limitless power of the Sun for use on Earth, freed from the limitations of nighttime, weather, and latitude. On a small scale, SBSP has immediate applications for powering military operations in remote locations as well as for disaster relief and rescue operations in areas without power. We need to stay ahead in this area, and China is moving quickly. Funding should be provided to the Space Force to develop and deploy a maneuverable one- to five-megawatt SBSP satellite to test this application and refine the technologies needed for larger scale commercial applications.

THE WORST-CASE SCENARIO

Testifying before the House Natural Resources Committee in December of 2023,[391] Dr. Greg Autry (coauthor) and Professor Michelle Hanlon, executive director of the Center for Air and Space Law at Ole Miss, were asked by Congressman Mike Collins of Georgia's Tenth Congressional District, "What is the worst-case scenario if China wins the race for space mining, and how will that impact the United States?"

> Dr. Autry: I don't want to be hyperbolic, but if China wins the race in space, we've ceded the strategic high ground militarily and ceded the entire economic future, and the United States will be relegated to a backwater position for the rest of human history. I honestly think this is an existential point.

> Prof. Hanlon: I agree with Dr. Autry. The Chinese will have the opportunity to block our access not just to the Moon but to all of space, and humanity's future lies in space. We have a lot of problems here on Earth to deal with

but a lot of the answers we will find in space,
including I believe ultimately, peace.

America and our free world allies can win Space Race 2.0, or we can fade into the obscurity of history as China's Communist Party ascends to the heavens. Humankind's future will be based either on the ideals of the Enlightenment or on "Xi Jinping Thought." There is no compromise middle road. This book was intended to get you, the public, to push your governmental representatives into swift, constructive, and consistent action supporting an effective American space policy. Make that visit, pick up that phone, send that email. Talk to your friends. As spaceflight controllers say before launch, "Go!"

LIST OF SPACE ABBREVIATIONS AND ACRONYMS

AFRL	Air Force Research Laboratory
AIAA	American Institute of Aeronautics and Astronautics
ARPA	Advance Projects Research Agency
ASAT	Anti-Satellite Weapon
AST	Office of Commercial Space Transportation (in FAA)
CASC	China Aerospace Science Corporation
CCDev	NASA's Commercial Crew Program
CCP	Chinese Communist Party
CGI	Computer-Generated Image
Cis-Lunar	The area around the Moon and Earth
CLD	Commercial LEO Destination, a commercial space station

CLPS	NASA's Commercial Lunar Payload Services
CME	Coronal Mass Ejection, a solar flare
CNSA	China National Space Administration, China's national space agency
COPUOS	UN Committee on the Peaceful Uses of Outer Space
COTS	Commercial Orbital Transportation Services
Cosmodrome	Soviet/Russian space launch facility in Kazakhstan
DoD	Department of Defense
DoT	Department of Transportation
DoC	Department of Commerce
EMP	Electromagnetic Pulse, a nuclear weapon used to degrade electronic systems
FAA	Federal Aviation Administration
FCC	Federal Communications Commission
EELV	Evolved Expendable Launch Vehicle

GEO	Geostationary Orbit, a special orbital ring 35,786 km above the equator, a distance at which satellites orbit at the same speed Earth turns, allowing them to hang at a fixed point in the sky
GPS	Global Positioning System
ICBM	Intercontinental Ballistic Missile
INSPA	In Space Production Applications, a NASA space manufacturing program
ISRO	India Space Research Organization, India's national space agency
ISS	The International Space Station
JWST	James Webb Space Telescope
Karman Line	An internationally accepted starting line for space at 100 km
L1–L5	Lagrange Points 1 through 5, gravitationally stable spots in the Earth–Moon system
LEO	Low Earth Orbit, where 90 percent of spacecraft operate, below 2,000 km
MEO	Medium Earth Orbit, 2,000–35,000 km

NASA	National Aeronautics and Space Administration, America's national space agency
NGO	Non-Governmental Organization, nonprofit
NOAA	National Oceanic and Atmospheric Administration
PARC	Palo Alto Research Center, a Xerox R&D lab
OSC	Office of Space Commerce
OST	Outer Space Treaty, primary international agreement on space
Roscosmos	Russia's space agency
SDI	Strategic Defense Initiative, Reagan-era space-based missile shield
SLS	Space Launch System, NASA's large rocket for Artemis
SRB	Solid Rocket Booster
SSP	Space Solar Power
STS	Space Transportation System, aka The Space Shuttle
ULA	United Launch Alliance, a joint venture of Boeing and Lockheed Martin
USAF	United States Air Force
USSF	United States Space Force
USSR	Union of Soviet Socialist Republics

RECOMMENDED RESOURCES

We hope you will find this book and the extensive reference citations to be useful sources for further information and research. Below are some of the resources we find useful, presented in no particular order.

BOOKS

Death by China, Peter Navarro and Greg Autry

Developing Space, John Strickland

Moon Rush, Dennis Wingo

Scramble for the Skies, Namrata Goswami and Peter Garretson

Thread of the Silkworm, Iris Chang

John F. Kennedy and the Race to the Moon, John M. Logsdon

After Apollo?: Richard Nixon and the American Space Program, John M. Logsdon

Ronald Reagan and the Space Frontier, John M. Logsdon

The Moon Is a Harsh Mistress, Robert A. Heinlein (science fiction)

The Three-Body Problem (三体), Liu Cixin (science fiction)

The Right Stuff, Tom Wolfe (novelization of history)

Lost Moon: The Perilous Voyage of Apollo 13, Jim Lovell

The High Frontier, Gerard K. O'Neill

The Case for Mars, Robert Zubrin

The Case for Space, Robert Zubrin

For All Moonkind, A Summary of Human History on the Moon, Michelle Hanlon

Space Law Quick Reference Booklet, University of Mississippi

Liftoff: Elon Musk and the Desperate Early Days that Launched SpaceX, Eric Berger

The Space Barons, Christian Davenport

The Space Economy, Chad Anderson

Space Is Open for Business, Robert Conway Jacobson

Escaping Gravity, Lori Garver

Falling Back to Earth: A First Hand Account of the Great Space Race and the End of the Cold War, Mark Albrecht

JOURNALS, MAGAZINES, WEBSITES

SpaceNews, https://spacenews.com

Space Policy Online, https://spacepolicyonline.com

Space.com, https://www.space.com

Payload, https://payloadspace.com/news/

LEOLabs Orbital Debris Visualizer, https://platform.leolabs.space/visualization

Encyclopedia Astronautica, http://www.astronautix.com

NASA Space Flight, https://www.nasaspaceflight.com

Gunter's Space Page, https://space.skyrocket.de/index.html

The Space Bucket, https://thespacebucket.com/wp-blog-overview/

NASA, https://www.nasa.gov

Ars Technica, https://arstechnica.com

The Space Review, https://www.thespacereview.com

ESA, https://www.esa.int

AmericaSpace, https://www.americaspace.com

ORGANIZATIONS

The National Space Society, https://nss.org

The Mars Society, https://www.marssociety.org

The Planetary Society, https://planetary.org

Moon Village Association, https://moonvillageassociation.org

For All Moonkind, https://www.forallmoonkind.org

The Space Frontier Foundation, https://spacefrontier.org

ENDNOTES

1   Thompson, Thomas. "Space Bomb in Color, Eerie Spectacle in the Pacific Sky," *LIFE*, July 20, 1962, https://books.google.com/books?id=KE4EAAAAMBAJ.

2   "Atomic Rainbow over Honolulu," Pearl Harbor Blast Zone, accessed July 6, 2023, https://pearl-harbor-blast-zone.blog-spot.com/2020/10/1962-atomic-rainbow-over-honolulu-was.html.

3   "A 'Quick Look' at the Technical Results of Starfish Prime," Department of Defense, August 1962, declassified March 16, 1989, 19, https://apps.dtic.mil/sti/pdfs/ADA955411.pdf.

4   Johnston, Wm. Robert. "High-Altitude Nuclear Explosions," January 28, 2009, http://www.johnstonsarchive.net/nuclear/hane.html.

5   Vittitoe, Charles N. "Did High-Altitude EMP Cause the Hawaiian Streetlight Incident?," System Design and Assessment Notes, Sandia National Laboratories, June 1989, http://ece-research.unm.edu/summa/notes/SDAN/0031.pdf.

6   "2022 Country Reports on Human Rights Practices: China," US Department of State, 2022, https://www.state.gov/reports/2022-country-reports-on-human-rights-practices/china/tibet/.

7   Graceffo, Antonio. "China's Crackdown on Mongolian Culture," *The Diplomat*, September 4, 2022, https://thediplomat.com/2020/09/chinas-crackdown-on-mongolian-culture/.

8   Boissoneault, Lorraine. "Is China Committing Genocide against the Uyghurs?," *Smithsonian Magazine*, February 2, 2022, https://www.smithsonianmag.com/history/is-china-committing-genocide-against-the-uyghurs-180979490/.

9   Pry, Peter Vincent. "China EMP Threat: The People's Republic of China Military Doctrine, Plans, and Capabilities for Electromagnetic Pulse (EMP) Attack," June 10, 2020, https://www.centerforsecuritypolicy.org/wp-content/uploads/2020/06/CHINAempTHREAT2020logo.pdf.

10   Higgins, Kelly Jackson. "Spear-Phishing Attacks Out of China Targeted Source Code, Intellectual Property," Dark Reading, January 13, 2010, https://www.darkreading.com/cyberattacks-data-breaches/spear-phishing-attacks-out-of-china-targeted-source-code-intellectual-property.

11   Navarro, Peter, and Greg Autry. *Death by China: Confronting the Dragon—A Global Call to Action* (Upper Saddle River, New Jersey: Pearson Prentice Hall, 2011).

12   Xuanzun, Liu. "US Intrusions in S. China Sea Can Be Stopped by Electromagnetic Weapons: Experts," *Global Times*, March 17, 2020, https://www.globaltimes.cn/content/1182886.shtml.

13   Lillis, Katie Bo et. al. "Exclusive: Russia attempting to develop nuclear space weapon to destroy satellites with massive energy wave, sources familiar with intel say," CNN, February 17, 2024, https://www.cnn.com/2024/02/16/politics/russia-nuclear-space-weapon-intelligence/index.html#.

14   Greenemeier, Larry. "GPS and the World's First 'Space War,'" *Scientific American*, February 8, 2016, https://www.scientificamerican.com/article/gps-and-the-world-s-first-space-war/.

15   Anderson, Eric et al. "China Dream, Space Dream," US-China Economic and Security Review Commission, accessed December 30, 2023, https://www.uscc.gov/sites/default/files/Research/China%20Dream%20Space%20Dream_Report.pdf.

16   Chi, Ma. "China Aims to Be World-Leading Space Power by 2045," *China Daily*, November 17, 2017, https://www.chinadaily.com.cn/china/2017-11/17/content_34653486.htm.

17   Hadley, Greg. "Saltzman: China's ASAT Test Was 'Pivot Point' in Space Operations," *Air & Space Forces Magazine*, January 13, 2023, https://www.airandspaceforces.com/saltzman-chinas-asat-test-was-pivot-point-in-space-operations/.

18   Vavrin, A. B. "Solar Cycle Sensitivity Study of Breakup Events in LEO," *Orbital Debris Quarterly*, NASA Orbital Debris Program Office, January 2015; "ISS Crew Take to Escape Capsules in Space Junk Alert," BBC, March 24, 2012, https://www.bbc.com/news/science-environment-17497766.

19   Johnson, Nick. "Orbital Debris: Operation Burnt Frost," NASA, May 16, 2014, https://sma.nasa.gov/vids/video-item/orbital-debris-operation-burnt-frost.

20   Galdorisi, George. "U.S. Navy Missile Defense: Operation Burnt Frost," Defense Media Network, May 18, 2013, https://www.defensemedianetwork.com/stories/u-s-navy-missile-defense-operation-burnt-frost/.

21   Amos, Johnathan. "Russian Anti-Satellite Missile Test Draws Condemnation," BBC, November 15, 2021, https://www.bbc.com/news/science-environment-59299101.

22   Goswami, Namrata, and Peter A. Garretson. *Scramble for the Skies: The Great Power Competition to Control the Resources of Outer Space* (Lanham, Maryland: Lexington Books, 2020).

23   Wall, Mike. "X-37B: The Air Force's Mysterious Space Plane," Space.com, August 30, 2021, https://www.space.com/25275-x37b-space-plane.html; Clark, Stephen. "In a Surprise Move, the Military's Spaceplane Will Launch on Falcon Heavy," Ars Technica, November 8, 2023, https://arstechnica.com/space/2023/11/in-a-surprise-move-the-militarys-spaceplane-will-launch-on-falcon-heavy/.

24   Brumfiel, Geoff. "New Chinese Space Plane Landed at Mysterious Air Base, Evidence Suggests," NPR, September 9, 2020, https://www.npr.org/2020/09/09/911113352/new-chinese-space-plane-landed-at-mysterious-air-base-evidence-suggests.

25   Salerno-Garthwaite, Andrew. "Is China's Korla Laser ASAT Site Hacking Western Satellites?," Army Technology, May 1, 2023, https://www.army-technology.com/features/is-chinas-korla-laser-asat-site-hacking-western-satellites/; Combined Air Operations Centre, "The Militarisation of Space: Disharmony in the Spheres," *Economist*, January 17, 2008, www.economist.com/node/10533205.

26 Hayes, Eli. "The Bohu Laser Facility, Part 1: History and Organisation," Arms Control Wonk, December 20, 2022, https://www.armscontrolwonk.com/archive/1216848/the-bohu-laser-facility-part-1-history-and-organisation/; Hayes, Eli. "The Bohu Laser Facility, Part 2: Operations," Arms Control Wonk, December 21, 2022, https://www.armscontrolwonk.com/archive/1216867/the-bohu-laser-facility-part-2-operations/.

27 Hua, Huang, et al. "Longtime Operation of S-Band Multi-Beam Relativistic Klystron Amplifier," 强激光与粒子束 34.11 (2022): 113001–1; Zhenbang, Liu, et al. "Design of X-Band High-Power High-Gain Multiple-Beam Relativistic Klystron Amplifier," 强激光与粒子束 32.10 (2020): 103004–1.

28 Chen, Stephen. "Chinese Team Powers Up Ultra-High Microwave Output: Paper," *South China Morning Post*, March 13, 2022, https://www.scmp.com/news/china/science/article/3170303/chinese-team-powers-ultra-high-microwave-output-paper.

29 Chen, Stephen. "The Powerful Chinese Megawatt Laser 'Small Enough for a Satellite,'" *South China Morning Post*, January 7, 2022, https://www.scmp.com/news/china/science/article/3162566/chinese-megawatt-laser-powerful-small-enough-be-used-satellite.

30 Honrada, Gabriel. "China Points Laser Sharp Threat at the Philippines," *Asia Times*, February 14, 2023, https://asiatimes.com/2023/02/china-points-laser-sharp-threat-at-the-philippines/.

31 "Subaru-Asahi Star Camera Captures Faint Green Laser Lights from Earth Observation Satellite," Subaru Telescope, Topics & Announcements, July 1, 2023, https://subarutelescope.org/en/news/topics/2023/02/15/3233.html.

32 Erwin, Sandra. "New U.S. Missile-Warning Satellite Set for Launch at Cape Canaveral," SpaceNews, January 16, 2018, https://www.space.com/39391-us-missile-warning-satellites-sbirs-geo-flight-4-launching-soon.html.

33 Pavur, James. "Securing New Space: On Satellite Cyber-Security" (PhD dissertation, University of Oxford, 2021).

34 Federal Bureau of Investigation, "VSAT Signals Vulnerable to Low-Cost Device Exploitation," FBI Private Industry Notification 20200214-001, February 14, 2020.

35 Urban, Mark. "Enthusiast Watches Nato Spy Pictures," BBC Newsnight, June 13 2002, http://news.bbc.co.uk/2/hi/programmes/newsnight/2041754.stm.

36 Wess, Mark. "ASAT Goes Cyber," Proceedings of the US Naval Institute, February 2021, https://www.usni.org/magazines/proceedings/2021/february/asat-goes-cyber.

37 "Space Attacks Open Database Project," Space & Cyber Security, accessed November 19, 2023, https://www.spacesecurity.info/en/space-attacks-open-database/.

38 Blinken, Antony. "Attribution of Russia's Malicious Cyber Activity against Ukraine," US Department of State Press Release, May 10, 2022, https://www.state.gov/attribution-of-russias-malicious-cyber-activity-against-ukraine/.

39 Musk, Elon (@elonmusk). Twitter (now X), May 10, 2022, https://x.com/elonmusk/status/1524191785760788480?s=20.

40 Horton, Alex. "Russia Tests Secretive Weapon to Target SpaceX's Starlink in Ukraine," *Washington Post*, April 18, 2023, https://www.washingtonpost.com/national-security/2023/04/18/discord-leaks-starlink-ukraine/.

41 Becker, Emily. "March 2015 ENSO Discussion: El Niño Is Here," ENSO Blog/NOAA, Mach 5, 2015, https://www.climate.gov/news-features/blogs/enso/march-2015-enso-discussion-el-niño-here.

42 Autry, Greg. "Space Research Can Save the Planet: Again," Foreign Policy, July 20, 2019, https://foreignpolicy.com/2019/07/20/space-research-can-save-the-planet-again-climate-change-environment/.

43 *Encyclopedia Britannica Online*, "Paleoclimate," accessed November 15, 2023, https://www.britannica.com/science/Cretaceous-Period/Paleoclimate.

44 Jensen, Jørn Bo, et al. "Early Holocene History of the Southwestern Baltic Sea: The Ancylus Lake Stage," *Boreas* 28.4 (1999): 437–453.

45 Herrle, Jens O., et al. "Black Sea Outflow Response to Holo-cene Meltwater Events," *Scientific Reports* 8.1 (2018): 4081.

46 Ballard, Robert D., et al. "Deepwater Archaeology of the Black Sea: The 2000 season at Sinop, Türkiye." *American Journal of Archaeology* 105.4 (2001): 607–623.

47 Cornish, Neil J. "What Is a Lagrange Point?," NASA, https://solarsystem.nasa.gov/resources/754/what-is-a-lagrange-point/.

48 Angel, Roger. "Feasibility of Cooling the Earth with a Cloud of Small Spacecraft Near the Inner Lagrange Point (L1)," *Proceedings of the National Academy of Sciences* 103.46 (2006): 17184–17189; Fuglesang, Christer, and María García de Herreros Miciano. "Realistic Sunshade System at L1 for Global Temperature Control," *Acta Astronautica* 186 (2021): 269–279.

49 Bromley, Benjamin C., Sameer H. Khan, and Scott J. Kenyon. "Dust As a Solar Shield," PLOS Climate 2.2 (2023): e0000133; Dorminey, Bruce. "Moondust Could Help Cool Earth's Climate, Say Researchers," *Forbes*, February, 9, 2023, https://www.forbes.com/sites/brucedorminey/2023/02/09/moon-dust-could-help-cool-earths-climate-say-researchers/?sh=-3783f2ea7cd0.

50 Green, James L., and Scott Boardsen. "Duration and Extent of the Great Auroral Storm of 1859," *Advances in Space Research* 38.2 (2006): 130–135.

51 Phillips, Tony. "The Great Québec Blackout," March 12, 2021, https://spaceweatherarchive.com/2021/03/12/the-great-que-bec-blackout/#:~:text=On%20March%2013%2C%201989%2C%20a%20powerful%20coronal%20mass,Ninety%20seconds%20later%2C%20the%20Hydro-Québec%20pow-er%20grid%20failed.

52 Schulte, Peter et al. "The Chicxulub Asteroid Impact and Mass Extinction at the Cretaceous-Paleogene Boundary," *Science* 327.5970 (2010): 1214–1218.

53 Amos, Jonathan. "Asteroid Strike Made 'Instant Himalayas,'" BBC News, November 18, 2016, https://www.bbc.com/news/science-environment-38019604.

54 Amos, Jonathan. "Dinosaur Asteroid Hit 'Worst Possible
Place,'" BBC News, May 15, 2017, https://www.bbc.com/news/
science-environment-39922998.

55 Robertson, Douglas S., et al. "Survival in the First Hours of
the Cenozoic," *Geological Society of America Bulletin* 116.5–6
(2004): 760–768.

56 Napier, W. M., and S. V. M. Clube. "A Theory of Terrestrial
Catastrophism," *Nature* 282 (1979): 455–459, https://doi.
org/10.1038/282455a0.

57 "Nemesis Star Theory: The Sun's 'Death Star' Companion,"
Space.com, accessed January 5, 2024, https://www.space.
com/22538-nemesis-star.html.

58 Popova, Olga P. et al. "Chelyabinsk Airburst, Damage Assessment, Meteorite Recovery, and Characterization," *Science*
342.6162 (2013): 1069–1073.

59 Число пострадавших при падении метеорита
приблизилось к 1500, РосБизнесКонсалтинг
[RBC], February 18, 2013, https://www.rbc.ru/society/18/02/2013/570403ae9a7947fcbd445cfd.

60 Farinella, Paolo et al. "Probable Asteroidal Origin of the Tunguska Cosmic Body," *Astronomy & Astrophysics* 377.3 (2001):
1081–1097.

61 Kennedy, Brian, and Alec Tyson. "Americans' Views of Space:
U.S. Role, NASA Priorities and Impact of Private Companies,"
Pew Research Center, July 20, 2023, https://www.pewresearch.
org/science/2023/07/20/americans-views-of-space-u-s-role-
nasa-priorities-and-impact-of-private-companies/.

62 Chapman, Clark R. "Statement on the Threat of Impact by
Near-Earth Asteroids," Subcommittee on Space and Aeronautics of the Committee on Science of the US House of
Representatives, May 21, 1998, https://www.boulder.swri.edu/
clark/hr.html; "Subtitle C—George E. Brown, Jr. Near-Earth
Object Survey," National Aeronautics and Space Administration Authorization Act of 2005, US House of Representatives,
December 30, 2005, https://www.govinfo.gov/content/pkg/
PLAW-109publ155/pdf/PLAW-109publ155.pdf.

63 Catalina Sky Survey, Lunar and Planetary Laboratory, University of Arizona, accessed July 25, 2023, https://catalina.lpl. arizona.edu.

64 "Once Again the Catalina Sky Survey Discovers an Earth-Impacting Asteroid," Lunar and Planetary Laboratory, University of Arizona, January 7, 2023, https://catalina.lpl.arizona.edu/ news/once-again-catalina-sky-survey-discovers-earth-impacting-asteroid.

65 "PanSTARRS: Astronomy & Asteroid Assessment," *Defense Industry Daily*, June 30, 2010, https://www.defenseindustrydaily. com/8M-for-Astronomy-Asteroid-Assessment-04828/.

66 Billings, Lee. "Alien Probe or Galactic Driftwood? SETI Tunes In to 'Oumuamua," *Scientific American*, December 11, 2017, https://www.scientificamerican.com/article/alien-probe-or-galactic-driftwood-seti-tunes-in-to-oumuamua/.

67 B612 Foundation, https://b612foundation.org.

68 Foust, Jeff. "NASA's DART Spacecraft Changes Asteroid's Orbit," SpaceNews, October 11, 2022, https://spacenews.com/ nasas-dart-spacecraft-changes-asteroids-orbit/.

69 "1969: The Internet's First Message Sent from UCLA," UCLA 100, accessed July 16, 2023, https://100.ucla.edu/timeline/the-internets-first-message-sent-from-ucla.

70 Markoff, John. "An Internet Pioneer Ponders the Next Revolution," *New York Times*, December 20, 1999, https://archive. nytimes.com/www.nytimes.com/library/tech/99/12/biztech/ articles/122099outlook-bobb.html.

71 NASA Spinoff, accessed July 16, 2023, https://spinoff.nasa. gov; Autry, Greg. "America's Investment in Space Pays Dividends," *Forbes*, July 9, 2017, https://www.forbes.com/sites/gregautry/2017/07/09/americas-investment-in-space-pays-dividends/.

72 Autry, Greg. "Solar Power: Capturing the Fruits for Our Labor," *Forbes*, January 4, 2018, https://www.forbes.com/sites/ gregautry/2018/01/04/solar-power-capturing-the-fruits-for-our-labor.

73 NASA, "Wind Energy Research Reaps Rewards," ScienceBlog, June 11, 2006, https://scienceblog.com/10780/wind-energy-research-reaps-rewards/.

74 "NOAA Satellites Helped Save 330 Lives in 2021," NOAA, January 31, 2022, https://www.noaa.gov/news-release/noaa-satellites-helped-save-330-lives-in-2021; Kinney, Joe. "GPS to the Rescue: How Tracking Technology Saves Lives," GPS Trackit, September 2, 2018, https://gpstrackit.com/blog/gps-to-the-rescue-how-tracking-technology-saves-lives/.

75 McTigue, Kathleen. "Economic Benefits of the Global Positioning System to the US Private Sector Study," National Institute of Standards and Technology, October 2, 2019, https://www.nist.gov/news-events/news/2019/10/economic-benefits-global-positioning-system-us-private-sector-study.

76 Autry, Greg. "Space Policy, Intergenerational Ethics, and the Environment," *AIAA SPACE 2011 Conference & Exposition*, 2011, http://www.gregautry.us/wp-content/uploads/Autry-AIAA-1.2.pdf.

77 "SSO," European Space Agency, March 2, 2020, https://www.esa.int/ESA_Multimedia/Images/2020/03/Polar_and_Sun-synchronous_orbit.

78 "Our Constellation," Planet, accessed September 9, 2023, https://www.planet.com/our-constellations/.

79 Erwin, Sandra. "Commercial Spy Satellites Put Russia's Ukraine Invasion in the Public Eye," SpaceNews, February 27, 2022, https://spacenews.com/satellite-imaging-companies-increase-profile-as-they-track-russias-invasion-of-ukraine/.

80 Erwin, Sandra. "Maxar Eager to Launch New Satellites amid Soaring Demand for Imagery over Ukraine," SpaceNews, April 11, 2022, https://spacenews.com/maxar-eager-to-launch-new-satellites-amid-soaring-demand-for-imagery-over-ukraine/.

81 Nakalembe, Catherine et al. "A Review of Satellite-Based Global Agricultural Monitoring Systems Available for Africa," *Global Food Security* 29 (June 2021): 100543.

82   "Satellite Imagery Helps Farmers Cut Water Use in Half,"
     NASA, October 7, 2020, https://landsat.gsfc.nasa.gov/arti-
     cle/satellite-imagery-helps-farmers-cut-water-use-in-half/;
     Charles, Dan. "Satellites Reveal the Secrets of Water-Guzzling
     Farms in California," NPR, October 18, 2021, https://www.
     npr.org/2021/10/18/1037371060/satellites-reveal-the-se-
     crets-of-water-guzzling-farms-in-california.

83   Benami, E. et al. "Uniting Remote Sensing, Crop Modelling
     and Economics for Agricultural Risk Management," *Nature
     Reviews, Earth & Environment* 2 (January 19, 2021): 140–159,
     https://doi.org/10.1038/s43017-020-00122-y.

84   Craig, Geoffery. "An Inside Look at SAR-Based Measure-
     ments," Ursa Space, October 9, 2020, https://ursaspace.com/
     blog/an-inside-look-at-sar-based-measurements/; Jensen,
     Eric. "Daily Analysis and Forecast of Global Oil Supplies,"
     ICEYE, October 21, 2021, https://www.iceye.com/blog/daily-
     analysis-and-forecast-of-global-oil-supplies.

85   Alpers, Werner, Benjamin Holt, and Kan Zeng. "Oil Spill
     Detection by Imaging Radars: Challenges and Pitfalls," *Remote
     Sensing of Environment* 201 (2017): 133–147.

86   Lem, Pola. "Peering through the Sands of Time," NASA,
     August 7, 2017, https://earthobservatory.nasa.gov/features/
     SpaceArchaeology.

87   Jenkins, Aric. "SpaceX Now Needs a License to Stream Earth
     from Orbit. Is Tesla's Starman to Blame?," *Fortune*, April 5,
     2018, https://fortune.com/2018/04/05/space-x-noaa-license-
     starman/.

88   Myre, Greg. "China Wants Your Data—And May Al-
     ready Have It," NPR, February 24, 2021, https://www.npr.
     org/2021/02/24/969532277/china-wants-your-data-and-may-
     already-have-it.

89   Pultarova, Tereza, and Elizabeth Howell. "Starlink Satellites:
     Everything You Need to Know about the Controversial Inter-
     net Megaconstellation," Space.com, August 2, 2023, https://
     www.space.com/spacex-starlink-satellites.html.

90 "China's Past Attempt to Take Over OneWeb Reportedly Investigated by UK Intelligence," Sputnik International, July 31, 2023, https://sputnikglobe.com/20230731/chinas-past-attempt-to-take-over-oneweb-reportedly-investigated-by-uk-intelligence-1112269548.html.

91 "UK Government Secures Satellite Network OneWeb," Gov. UK, November 20, 2020, https://www.gov.uk/government/news/uk-government-secures-satellite-network-oneweb.

92 Abbas, Muntazir. "Centre to Examine Chinese Stakeholding after OneWeb–Eutelsat Merger," Satcom/*India Times*, November 27, 2022, https://telecom.economictimes.indiatimes.com/news/oneweb-eutelsat-merger-under-government-scrutiny/95756253.

93 "FCC Authorizes Kuiper Satellite Constellation," FCC, July 30, 2020, https://www.fcc.gov/document/fcc-authorizes-kuiper-satellite-constellation.

94 Clark, Stephen. "A Bitter Pill: Amazon Calls on Rival SpaceX to Launch Internet Satellites," Ars Technica, December 1, 2023, https://arstechnica.com/space/2023/12/a-bitter-pill-amazon-calls-on-rival-spacex-to-launch-internet-satellites/.

95 "What We Do," Lynk, accessed September 10, 2023, https://lynk.world/what-we-do/.

96 Coldewey, Devin. "Lynk Connects Palau's Off-Grid Islands with Satellite Texting," TechCrunch, June 26, 2023, https://techcrunch.com/2023/06/26/lynk-connects-palaus-off-grid-islands-with-satellite-texting/.

97 Coauthor Greg Autry in conversation with Charles Miller.

98 Freeman, Christopher, H. S. D. Cole, and Marie Jahoda, eds., *Models of Doom: A Critique of* The Limits to Growth" (New York: Universe Books, 1973).

99 "Another Ice Age?," *TIME*, June 24, 1974, (via Internet Archive), https://web.archive.org/web/20070311092656/http://www.time.com/time/magazine/article/0,9171,944914,00.html.

100 Schneider, Stephen H. "Against Instant Books," *Nature*, December 1977, http://stephenschneider.stanford.edu/Publications/PDF_Papers/Schneider1977.pdf.

101 Maughan, Tim. "The Dystopian Lake Filled by the World's Tech Lust," BBC, April 2, 2015, https://www.bbc.com/future/article/20150402-the-worst-place-on-earth.

102 Georgilidakis, Spyros. "SR-71: When CIA Used Soviet Titanium to Spy on USSR," Mentour Pilot, https://mentourpilot.com/sr-71-when-cia-used-soviet-titanium-to-spy-on-ussr/.

103 Jet Propulsion Laboratory, "How NASA's Psyche Mission Will Explore an Unexplored World," NASA, December 20, 2021, https://www.nasa.gov/solar-system/how-nasas-psyche-mission-will-explore-an-unexplored-world/.

104 Shea, Dana A., and Daniel Morgan. "The Helium-3 Shortage: Supply, Demand, and Options for Congress," Congressional Research Service, December 22, 2010, https://sgp.fas.org/crs/misc/R41419.pdf.

105 Bob, Yonah Jeremy. "Ex-CIA Officer Talks US–China Space Wars on Solar, Fusion Energy, Mining," *Jerusalem Post*, November 4, 2021, https://www.jpost.com/international/ex-cia-officer-talks-us-china-space-wars-on-solar-fusion-energy-mining-683936.

106 Fa, W., and Y. Jin. "Global Inventory of Helium-3 in Lunar Regoliths Estimated by a Multi-Channel Microwave Radiometer on the Chang-E 1 Lunar Satellite," *China Science Bulletin* 55 (December 10, 2010): 4005–4009, https://doi.org/10.1007/s11434-010-4198-9.

107 Makichuk, Dave. "Helium-3: The Secret 'Mining War' in Space," *Asia Times*, November 6, 2021, https://asiatimes.com/2021/11/helium-3-the-secret-mining-war-in-space/.

108 Bob, Yonah Jeremy. "Ex-CIA Officer Talks US–China Space Wars on Solar, Fusion Energy, Mining," *Jerusalem Post*, November 4, 2021, https://www.jpost.com/international/ex-cia-officer-talks-us-china-space-wars-on-solar-fusion-energy-mining-683936.

109 Howell, Elizabeth. "Shoemaker-Levy 9: Comet's Impact Left Its Mark on Jupiter," January 23, 2018, https://www.space.com/19855-shoemaker-levy-9.html.

110 "Europa: Water World Infographic," NASA, January 9,
     2019, https://europa.nasa.gov/resources/148/europa-wa-
     ter-world-infographic/.

111 Mehta, Jatan. "Your Guide to Water on the Moon," The
     Planetary Society, August 6, 2022, https://www.planetary.org/
     articles/water-on-the-moon-guide.

112 Sutton, Kelsey. "Trump Jokes with Astronauts on Reusing
     Human Waste," Politico, April 24, 2017, https://www.politico.
     com/story/2017/04/24/trump-astronauts-press-confer-
     ence-237522.

113 Zimmer, Katarina. "Pharma Looks to Outer Space to Boost
     Drug R&D," The Scientist, December 1, 2020, https://www.
     the-scientist.com/bio-business/pharma-looks-to-outer-
     space-to-boost-drug-rd--68183.

114 Smith, Rick. "NASA, Industry Partner for Space-Based Study
     of Potential Alzheimer's Key," The Marshall Star, October 30,
     2019, https://www.nasa.gov/centers-and-facilities/marshall/
     the-marshall-star-130/.

115 Murdan, S. et al. "Immobilisation of Vaccines onto Mi-
     cro-Crystals for Enhanced Thermal Stability," International
     Journal of Pharmaceutics (May 30, 2005), https://pubmed.
     ncbi.nlm.nih.gov/15885463/.

116 Petroleka, Marina, and Laura Attwood, "Why Is Big Pharma
     Interested in the Space Economy?," WhyForum/FitchRatings,
     June 14, 2018 (via Internet Archive), https://web.archive.org/
     web/20190708014715/https://medium.com/fitch-blog/why-
     is-big-pharma-interested-in-the-space-economy-c078ac1b-
     f67c.

117 Redwire. "Redwire Opens New Commercial Market for In
     Space Production with First Sale of Space-Manufactured
     Optical Crystal," June 23, 2022, https://redwirespace.com/
     newsroom/redwire-opens-new-commercial-market-for-in-
     space-production-with-first-sale-of-space-manufactured-op-
     tical-crystal/.

118 Werner, Debra. "Flawless Photonics Kicking Glass," SpaceNews, February 23, 2024 https://spacenews.com/flawless-photonics-kicking-glass/.

119 Barber, Gregory. "The Best Place to Make Undersea Cables Might Be in Space," *Wired*, September 11, 2019, https://www.wired.com/story/the-best-place-to-make-undersea-cables-might-be-in-space/#.

120 ISS National Laboratory, "Stanford University Sends Semiconductor Investigation to the International Space Station," June 8, 2023, https://www.issnationallab.org/spx28-stanford-semiconductor-crystals/.

121 Triolo, T. J. "Taking Semiconductor Manufacturing to New Heights," ASU News, September 15, 2023, https://news.asu.edu/20230915-discoveries-taking-semiconductor-manufacturing-new-heights.

122 "Life of a Foam," European Space Agency, June 12, 2019, https://www.esa.int/Science_Exploration/Human_and_Robotic_Exploration/Life_of_a_foam.

123 Sakai, Naomichi et al. "Fabrication of Large-Grain Bulk Superconductors in Microgravity Environment," *Acta Astronautica* 53.1 (July 2003): 35–43.

124 Grimm, Daniela et al. "The Effects of Microgravity on Differentiation and Cell Growth in Stem Cells and Cancer Stem Cells," *Stem Cells Translational Medicine* 9.8 (2020): 882–894; Sims, Josh. "Why Astronauts Are Printing Organs in Space," BBC, June 1, 2021, https://www.bbc.com/future/article/20210601-how-transplant-organs-might-be-printed-in-outer-space.

125 "NASA Makes Award for In-Space Liver Tissue Manufacturing Demonstration," NASA InSPA, August 21, 2023, https://www.nasa.gov/feature/nasa-makes-award-for-in-space-liver-tissue-manufacturing-demonstration.

126 Hughes, Susie et al. "Killing Prisoners for Transplants: Forced Organ Harvesting in China," The Conversation, July 28, 2022, https://theconversation.com/killing-pris-

oners-for-transplants-forced-organ-harvesting-in-chi-
na-161999.

127 "Redwire BioFabrication Facility Successfully Prints First
Human Knee Meniscus on ISS," Redwire, September 7, 2023,
https://redwirespace.com/newsroom/redwire-biofabrica-
tion-facility-successfully-prints-first-human-knee-menis-
cus-on-iss-paving-the-way-for-advanced-in-space-bioprint-
ing-capabilities-to-benefit-human-health/.

128 "An Artificial Retina Engineered from Ancient Protein Heads
to Space," National Eye Institute, April 12, 2021, https://www.
nei.nih.gov/about/news-and-events/news/artificial-reti-
na-engineered-ancient-protein-heads-space.

129 Guzman, Ana. "Crew-4 Astronauts Head to Space Station
to Conduct Microgravity Science," NASA, April 18, 2022,
https://www.nasa.gov/mission_pages/station/research/crew-
4-head-to-iss-microgravity-science.

130 NASA, "Fighting Cancer with Microgravity Research,"
Technology Org, June 25, 2013, https://www.technology.
org/2013/06/25/fighting-cancer-with-microgravity-research/.

131 Topal, Uğur, and Cihan Zamur. "Microgravity, Stem Cells,
and Cancer: A New Hope for Cancer Treatment," *Stem Cells
International* (2021).

132 Ibid.

133 Clayton, James. "SpaceX: Can Meat Be Grown in Space?,"
BBC, April 25, 2022, https://www.bbc.com/news/technolo-
gy-61116018.

134 Hu, Wenrui, and Qi Kang, eds. *Physical Science Under Microgravity: Experiments on Board the SJ-10 Recoverable Satellite*
(Singapore: Springer, 2019).

135 Yin, Zhigang et al. "Melt Growth of Semiconductor Crystals
Under Microgravity," *Physical Science Under Microgravity:
Experiments on Board the SJ-10 Recoverable Satellite* (Singa-
pore: Springer, 2019): 327–360.

136 "SJ 10," NASA, October 28, 2022, https://nssdc.gsfc.nasa.gov/
nmc/spacecraft/display.action?id=2016-023E.

137 "NASA Selects Proposals for In-Space Development of Projects Including Optical Fibers and Stem Cells and a Plan to Enable a Low Earth Orbit Economy," NASA, April 7, 2020, https://www.nasa.gov/leo-economy/nasa-selects-for-projects-optical-fibers-stem-cells-enable-low-earth-orbit-economy.

138 "In Space Production Applications," NASA, accessed September 30, 2023, https://www.nasa.gov/international-space-station/space-station-research-and-technology/in-space-production-applications/.

139 "On-Orbit Servicing, Assembly, and Manufacturing 2," NASA, accessed November 29, 2023, https://www.nasa.gov/mission/on-orbit-servicing-assembly-and-manufacturing-2-osam-2/.

140 Werner, Debra. "Made in Space Highlights Defense Applications for Manufacturing and Robotic Assembly Technology," SpaceNews, August 3, 2020, https://spacenews.com/made-in-space-national-security/.

141 Perlin, John. "The Story of Vanguard," UCSB Experimental Cosmology Group, 2023, https://www.deepspace.ucsb.edu/outreach/the-space-race/the-story-of-vanguard.

142 Autry, Greg. "Solar Power: Capturing the Fruits for Our Labor," *Forbes*, January 4, 2018, https://www.forbes.com/sites/gregautry/2018/01/04/solar-power-capturing-the-fruits-for-our-labor.

143 Gates, Bill. "Innovating to Zero," TED, February 2010, https://www.ted.com/talks/bill_gates_innovating_to_zero.

144 Pultarova, Tereza. "Can Space-Based Solar Power Really Work? Here Are the Pros and Cons," Space.com, December 23, 2022, https://www.space.com/space-solar-power-pros-cons.

145 "Power Beaming Comes of Age," *MIT Technology Review*, October 6, 2022, https://www.technologyreview.com/2022/10/06/1060650/power-beaming-comes-of-age/; "Tesla's Wireless Power," Tesla Science Center, accessed De-

cember 19, 2023, https://teslasciencecenter.org/teslas-wire-less-power/.

146 Choi, Charles Q. "DARPA Hopes to Beam Power across 200 Kilometers," IEEE Spectrum, October 20, 2023, https://spectrum.ieee.org/power-beaming-2665745442.

147 David, Leonard. "Peter Glaser, Father of Solar-Power Satellite Idea, Dies at 90," Space.com, June 09, 2014, https://www.space.com/26175-peter-glaser-solar-power-satellite-obituary.html.

148 Mankins, John. *The Case for Space Solar Power* (Virginia Edition Publishing, 2014).

149 Volta Space, accessed December 20, 2023, https://www.voltaspace.co.

150 Needham, Kristy. "Plans for First Chinese Solar Power Station in Space Revealed," *Sydney Morning Herald*, February 15, 2019, https://www.smh.com.au/world/asia/plans-for-first-chinese-solar-power-station-in-space-revealed-20190214-p50xtg.html.

151 Jones, Andrew. "China Aims for Space-Based Solar Power Test in LEO in 2028, GEO in 2030," SpaceNews, June 8, 2022, https://spacenews.com/china-aims-for-space-based-solar-power-test-in-leo-in-2028-geo-in-2030/.

152 Rosenbaum, Eric. "China Plans a Solar Power Play in Space That NASA Abandoned Decades Ago," CNBC.com, March 17, 2019, https://www.cnbc.com/2019/03/15/china-plans-a-solar-power-play-in-space-that-nasa-abandoned-long-ago.html.

153 Dong, S., H. Xinbin, and X. Wang, "Retro-Directive Microwave Power Beam Steering Technology for Space Solar Power Station," *Chinese Space Science and Technology* 42.5 (2022): 91.

154 Rosenbaum, Eric. "China Plans a Solar Power Play in Space That NASA Abandoned Decades Ago," CNBC.com, March 17, 2019, https://www.cnbc.com/2019/03/15/china-plans-a-solar-power-play-in-space-that-nasa-abandoned-long-ago.html.

155 "Microwave Weapon Suspected of Mystery Attacks on US Diplomats in China and Cuba," Agence France-Presse via *South China Morning Post*, September 3, 2018, https://www.scmp.com/news/world/united-states-canada/article/2162447/report-microwave-weapon-suspected-mystery-attacks-us.

156 Makichuk, Dave. "Did China Use Microwave Weapons on Indian Soldiers?," *Asia Times*, November 18, 2020, https://asiatimes.com/2020/11/did-china-use-microwave-weapons-on-indian-soldiers/; Peck, Michael. "The Pentagon Fears That Deadly Microwave Weapons Are Undetectable," *Forbes*, March 2, 2021, https://www.forbes.com/sites/michaelpeck/2021/03/02/the-pentagon-fears-that-deadly-microwave-weapons-are-undetectable.

157 Tang, Didi. "China Turns Ladakh Battleground with India into a 'Microwave Oven,'" *Times of London*, November 17, 2020, https://www.thetimes.co.uk/article/china-turns-ladakh-battleground-with-india-into-a-microwave-oven-6tlwtrtzz.

158 "Active Denial System FAQs," Joint Intermediate Force Capabilities Office, US Department of Defense Non-Lethal Weapons Program, accessed December 2, 2023, https://jnlwp.defense.gov/About/Frequently-Asked-Questions/Active-Denial-System-FAQs.

159 Griffiths, Robbie. "Ditch the Rockets and Help the Planet, Greta Thunberg Urges Elon Musk," *Standard*, October 31, 2022, https://www.standard.co.uk/news/londoners-diary/londoners-diary-greta-thunberg-elon-musk-liz-truss-maya-jama-henry-cavill-b1036415.html; Liberatore, Stacy. "Greta Thunberg Releases Satirical Mars Tourism Ad for Richest 'One Percent to Start Again on an Untainted Planet' and Leave the Rest of Us to 'Fix Climate Change,'" *Daily Mail*, February 17, 2021, https://www.dailymail.co.uk/sciencetech/article-9271483/Greta-Thurnberg-releases-satirical-Mars-tourism-ad-telling-one-percent-escape-planet.html.

160 "Mars & Beyond," SpaceX.com, accessed December 4, 2023, https://www.spacex.com/humanspaceflight/mars.

161 Powell, Corey S. "Jeff Bezos Foresees a Trillion People Living in Millions of Space Colonies. Here's What He's Doing to Get the Ball Rolling," NBC News, May 15, 2019, https://www.nbcnews.com/mach/science/jeff-bezos-foresees-trillion-people-living-millions-space-colonies-here-ncna1006036.

162 Trump, Donald J. "Reinvigorating America's Human Space Exploration Program," December 11, 2017, https://trumpwhitehouse.archives.gov/presidential-actions/presidential-memorandum-reinvigorating-americas-human-space-exploration-program/.

163 Neufeld, Michael J. "Weimar Culture and Futuristic Technology: The Rocketry and Spaceflight Fad in Germany, 1923–1933," *Technology and Culture*, vol. 31, no. 4 (October 1990): 725–52, https://doi.org/10.2307/3105905.

164 Oberth, Hermann. *The Rocket into Planetary Space* (Walter de Gruyter GmbH & Co. KG, 2014).

165 Giaimo, Cara. "NASA Stole the Rocket Countdown from a 1929 Fritz Lang Film," Atlas Obscura, February 1, 2016, https://www.atlasobscura.com/articles/nasa-stole-the-rocket-countdown-from-a-1929-fritz-lang-film-1d569cc0-50ff-4045-b0c9-1f0d72a193db.

166 "Robert Hutchings Goddard," Genesis, Search for Origins, NASA Biographies, accessed December 4, 2023, https://solarsystem.nasa.gov/genesismission/people/biographies/goddard.pdf.

167 "Dr. Robert H. Goddard," NASA, accessed December 3, 2023, https://www.nasa.gov/dr-robert-h-goddard-american-rocketry-pioneer/.

168 Crouch, Tom D. "Reaching Toward Space," *Smithsonian*, February 2001, https://www.smithsonianmag.com/science-nature/reaching-toward-space-37458291/.

169 Nelson, Craig. *Rocket Men: The Epic Story of the First Men on the Moon* (New York: Penguin, 2009).

170 Benson, Michael. "Science Fiction Sent Man to the Moon," *New York Times*, July 20, 2019, https://www.nytimes.com/2019/07/20/opinion/sunday/moon-rockets-space-fiction.html.

171 Tsiolkovsky, K. S. "Exploration of Outer Space by Means of Rocket Devices," *The Science Review* 5 (1903).

172 "History & Heritage," AIAA, accessed December 4, 2023, https://www.aiaa.org/about/History-and-Heritage.

173 Neufeld, Michael J. *The Rocket and the Reich: Peenemünde and the Coming of the Ballistic Missile Era* (New York: Simon and Schuster, 1995), 190–191.

174 Ptak, John. "Did We Hit the Wrong Planet?," post 2084, accessed December 6, 2023, https://longstreet.typepad.com/thesciencebookstore/2013/08/did-we-hit-the-wrong-planet-w-von-braun-1956.html.

175 Winter, Frank H. "Robert Goddard Was the Father of American Rocketry. But Did He Have Much Impact?," *Smithsonian Air and Space Magazine*, May 8, 2018, https://www.smithsonianmag.com/air-space-magazine/robert-goddard-was-father-american-rocketry-did-he-have-much-impact-180969029/.

176 Siddiqi, Asif. "Sliver Bird," Huntington Verso, August 18, 2016, https://huntington.org/verso/silver-bird.

177 Reichhardt, Tony. "The First Photo from Space," *Smithsonian Air and Space Magazine*, October 24, 2006, https://www.smithsonianmag.com/air-space-magazine/the-first-photo-from-space-13721411/.

178 Gray, Tara. "A Brief History of Animals in Space," NASA, January 18, 1998, https://history.nasa.gov/animals.html.

179 Ordway, Frederick Ira, and Mitchell R. Sharpe, *The Rocket Team*, 2nd ed. (Burlington, Ontario: Apogee Books, 2008), 402.

180 Eckles, Jim. "Two Crashes in Two Weeks: In 1947, Rockets Launched from White Sands Landed in Alamogordo, Juárez," *Las Cruces Sun News*, May 15, 2022, https://www.lcsun-news.

com/story/life/2022/05/15/1947-rockets-launched-white-sands-landed-alamogordo-juarez/9740356002/.

181 Ordway, Frederick Ira, and Mitchell R. Sharpe, *The Rocket Team*, 2nd ed. (Burlington, Ontario: Apogee Books, 2008), 402.

182 Powell-Willhite, Irene E., ed., *The Voice of Dr. Wernher von Braun: An Anthology* (Burlington, Ontario: Apogee Books, 2007).

183 Foust, Jeff. "Review: The Voice of Wernher von Braun," August 6, 2007, The Space Review, https://www.thespacereview.com/article/923/1.

184 Spitzmiller, Ted. "Book Review: Project Mars," National Space Society, January 27, 2010, https://space.nss.org/book-review-project-mars/.

185 "Man and the Moon," Internet Movie Database (IMDB), accessed December 8, 2023, https://www.imdb.com/title/tt0351298/.

186 "Atom Spy Case/Rosenbergs," FBI, accessed December 8, 2023, https://www.fbi.gov/history/famous-cases/atom-spy-caserosenbergs; Radosh, Ronald. "Case Closed: The Rosenbergs Were Soviet Spies," June 4, 2015, *Los Angeles Times*, https://www.latimes.com/la-oe-radosh17-2008sep17-story.html.

187 "Qian Xuesen," Caltech Graduate Aerospace Laboratories, accessed December 8, 2023, https://www.galcit.caltech.edu/about/legends-of-galcit/qian-xuesen-tsien-hsue-shen.

188 "Qian Xuesen," Caltech Graduate Aerospace Laboratories, accessed December 16, 2023, https://www.galcit.caltech.edu/about/legends-of-galcit/qian-xuesen-tsien-hsue-shen.

189 "Qian Xuesen: The Man the US Deported—Who Then Helped China into Space," BBC, October 26, 2020, https://www.bbc.com/news/stories-54695598.

190 Chang, Iris. *The Thread of the Silkworm* (Basic Books, 1995).

191 Sergei P. Korolev, International Space Hall of Fame, New Mexico Museum of Space History, https://www.nmspacemuseum.org/inductee/sergei-p-korolev/.

192 Harford, James. *Korolev: How One Man Masterminded the Soviet Drive to Beat America to the Moon* (Hoboken, New Jersey, John Wiley & Sons, 1997).

193 "Sergei Korolev: Father of the Soviet Union's Success in Space," European Space Agency, March 9, 2007, https://www.esa.int/About_Us/ESA_history/50_years_of_humans_in_space/Sergei_Korolev_Father_of_the_Soviet_Union_s_success_in_space.

194 Harford, James. *Korolev: How One Man Masterminded the Soviet Drive to Beat America to the Moon* (Hoboken, New Jersey, John Wiley & Sons 1997).

195 Chertok, Boris Evseevich. *Rockets and People Volume II: Creating a Rocket Industry* (Washington, DC: National Aeronautics and Space Administration, 2006), 119.

196 Chang, Iris. *The Thread of the Silkworm* (Basic Books, 1995).

197 Muszyński-Sulima, Wawrzyniec. "Cold War in Space: Reconnaissance Satellites and US-Soviet Security Competition," *European Journal of American Studies* 18.18-2 (2023).

198 Yuri's Night, accessed December 8, 2023, https://yurisnight.net.

199 Wolfe, Tom. *The Right Stuff* (New York: Random House, 1979).

200 Smithsonian, "Mercury Primate Capsule and Ham the Astrochimp," Under the Radar, November 10, 2015, https://airandspace.si.edu/stories/editorial/mercury-primate-capsule-and-ham-astrochimp.

201 Neufeld, Michael. "Enos: the Forgotten Chimp," Smithsonian National Air and Space Museum, November 29, 2021, https://airandspace.si.edu/stories/editorial/enos-forgotten-chimp.

202 Evans, Michelle. "The X-15 Rocket Plane, Flying the First Wings into Space," 2020, http://www.mach25media.com/Resources/X15FlightLog.pdf.

203 "X-15B," Astronautix.com, accessed December 19, 2023, http://www.astronautix.com/x/x-15b.html.

204 Krulwich, Robert. "A Cosmonaut's Fiery Death Retold," NPR, May 3, 2011, https://www.npr.org/blogs/krulwich/2011/05/03/135919389/a-cosmonauts-fiery-death-retold.

205 Evans, Ben. "'For the Tenth Time': The Story of Soyuz 4 and 5," AmericaSpace, accessed December 18, 2023, https://www.americaspace.com/2014/01/04/for-the-tenth-time-the-story-of-soyuz-4-5-part-1/.

206 "N1," Astronautix.com, accessed December 18, 2023, http://www.astronautix.com/n/n1.html.

207 Logsdon, John M. "The Moon Race," in *A Companion to John F. Kennedy*, ed. Marc J. Selverstone (John Wiley & Sons, 2014), 478–495; Logsdon, John M. *John F. Kennedy and the Race to the Moon* (New York: Palgrave Macmillan, 2010).

208 Uri, John. "60 Years Ago: President Kennedy Proposes Moon Landing Goal in Speech to Congress," NASA, May 25, 2021, https://www.nasa.gov/history/60-years-ago-president-kennedy-proposes-moon-landing-goal-in-speech-to-congress/.

209 OMB and NASA budget data, summarized at: USAFacts Team, "50 Years after the Apollo 11 Moon Landing, Here's a Look at NASA's Budget throughout Its History," USAFacts, December 2, 2019, https://usafacts.org/articles/50-years-after-apollo-11-moon-landing-heres-look-nasas-budget-throughout-its-history/.

210 Autry, Greg. "Pennywise, Future Foolish: Congress Moves to Cut NASA Science Budget," *Forbes*, July 27, 2023, https://www.forbes.com/sites/gregautry/2023/07/27/pennywise-future-foolish-congress-moves-to-cut-nasa-science-budget.

211 Uri, John. "55 Years Ago: Tragedy on the Launch Pad," NASA, January 27, 2022, https://www.nasa.gov/history/55-years-ago-tragedy-on-the-launch-pad/.

212 Nelson, Craig. *Rocket Men: The Epic Story of the First Men on the Moon* (New York: Penguin, 2009).

213 Stamm, Amy. "'One Small Step for Man' or 'a Man'?," Smithsonian National Air and Space Museum, July 17, 2019,

https://airandspace.si.edu/stories/editorial/one-small-step-man-or-man.

214 Cass, Stephen. "Apollo 13, We Have a Solution," *IEEE Spectrum*, April 2005, (via Internet Archive), https://web.archive.org/web/20120813184401/http://spectrum.ieee.org/aerospace/space-flight/apollo-13-we-have-a-solution-part-2/3.

215 Portree, David S. "Ending Apollo (1968)," *Wired*, September 22, 2013, https://www.wired.com/2013/09/ending-apollo-1968/.

216 Day, Dwayne A. "Negative Symbolism, or Why America Will Continue to Fly Astronauts," *The Space Review*, January 16, 2006, https://www.thespacereview.com/article/535/1.

217 Ezell, Edward C., and Linda N. Ezell. "The Partnership: A History of the Apollo-Soyuz Test Project," NASA, 1978, https://www.nasa.gov/wp-content/uploads/2023/04/sp-4209.pdf.

218 Autry, Greg. "Safety Last: Reckless Behavior Provides China with Economic Competitive Advantages in Space Launch," SpaceNews, May 21, 2019, https://spacenews.com/safety-last-reckless-behavior-provides-china-with-economic-competitive-advantages-in-space-launch/.

219 "Report to Congress," Comptroller General of the United States, June 2, 1972 (see appendix I, page 49, letter from Senator Walter F. Mondale), http://archive.gao.gov/f0302/096542.pdf.

220 Jones, Harry. "The Recent Large Reduction in Space Launch Cost," *48th International Conference on Environmental Systems*, July 2018, https://ntrs.nasa.gov/api/citations/20200001093/downloads/20200001093.pdf.

221 Leinfelder, Andrea. "40 Years after Its Pioneering Launch, NASA's Space Shuttle Leaves a 'Mixed Legacy.' Was It Worth It?," *Houston Chronicle*, April 10, 2021, https://www.houstonchronicle.com/news/houston-texas/space/article/40-years-after-its-pioneering-launch-NASA-s-16086053.php.

222 Logsdon, John M. *After Apollo?: Richard Nixon and the American Space Program* (New York: Springer, 2015).

223 Avilla, Aeryn. "California Dreamin': Vandenberg AFB & the Space Shuttle," Spaceflight Histories, July 15, 2021, https://www.spaceflighthistories.com/post/vandenberg-space-shuttle.

224 Heppenheimer, T. A. *The Space Shuttle Decision*, Chapter 5, "Shuttle to the Forefront," 1999, https://history.nasa.gov/SP-4221/ch5.htm.

225 Lewis, Cathleen. "The Soviet Buran Shuttle: One Flight, Long History," Smithsonian Air and Space Museum, November 15, 2013, https://airandspace.si.edu/stories/editorial/soviet-buran-shuttle-one-flight-long-history.

226 Jenkins, Dennis R. *Space Shuttle: Developing an Icon: 1972–2013* (Specialty Press, 2016).

227 Homer, Courtney V. K. "Spies in Space: Reflections on Reconnaissance and the Manned Orbiting Laboratory," National Reconnaissance Office, May 2019, https://www.nro.gov/Portals/65/documents/history/csnr/programs/Spies_In_Space-Reflections_on_MOL_web.pdf.

228 Uri, John. "50 Years Ago: Launch of Salyut, the World's First Space Station," NASA, April 19, 2021, https://www.nasa.gov/missions/station/50-years-ago-launch-of-salyut-the-worlds-first-space-station/.

229 Belew, Leland, and Ernst Stuhlinger. *Skylab: A Guidbook*, NASA, 1973, https://history.nasa.gov/EP-107/contents.htm.

230 "Skylab's Fiery Fall," *TIME*, July 16, 1979, (via Internet Archive), https://web.archive.org/web/20070213023709/http://www.time.com/time/printout/0,8816,920502,00.html

231 Siemer, Hannah. "Littering Fine Paid," *Esperance Express*, April 17, 2009, https://archive.ph/20120711163508/http://esperance.yourguide.com.au/news/local/news/general/littering-fine-paid/1488319.aspx?storypage=1.

232 Zak, Anatoly. "Remembering That Time the Soviet Union Shot a Top-Secret Space Cannon While in Orbit," *Popular Mechanics*, October 24, 2022. https://www.popularmechanics.com/military/weapons/a18187/here-is-the-soviet-unions-secret-space-cannon/.

233 "Mir," Astroanutix.com, accessed December 21, 2023, http://www.astronautix.com/m/mir.html.

234 Hall, R. *The History of Mir, 1986–2000* (British Interplanetary Society, 2000).

235 Avilla, Aeryn. "Space Station Freedom: The Bridge between Skylab and the ISS," Spaceflight Histories, August 13, 2020, https://www.spaceflighthistories.com/post/space-station-freedom.

236 Uri, John. "Space Station 20th: Historical Origins of ISS," NASA, January 23, 2020, https://www.nasa.gov/history/space-station-20th-historical-origins-of-iss/.

237 Davies, Francis. "Overview of International Space Station Electrical Power System," NASA Johnson Space Center, November 2016, https://ntrs.nasa.gov/api/citations/20160014034/downloads/20160014034.pdf; Speck, Emilee. "The International Space Station Is about to Get Major Power Upgrade," Click Orlando, June 15, 2021, https://www.clickorlando.com/news/local/2021/06/01/the-international-space-station-is-about-to-get-major-power-upgrade/.

238 Lafleur, Claude. "Cost of US Piloted Programs," *Space Review*, March 8, 2010, https://www.thespacereview.com/article/1579/1.

239 Coauthor (Autry) observation during reviews of NASA budgets while working with NASA Headquarters in 2016 (agency review team), 2017 (White House liaison), and 2020 (CFO nominee).

240 Berthe, Philippe et al. "Orion European Service Module (ESM) Development, Integration and Qualification Status," *2018 AIAA SPACE and Astronautics Forum and Exposition*, 2018, https://ntrs.nasa.gov/api/citations/20170009574/downloads/20170009574.pdf.

241 Young, Chris. "Surprise! NASA Wants to Commercialize the ISS before Its 'Deorbit' in 2031," *Interesting Engineering*, February 03, 2022, https://interestingengineering.com/innovation/nasa-iss-deorbit.

242   Coauthor (Autry) observation during reviews of NASA budgets while working with NASA.

243   Foust, Jeff. "NASA Revises Contract Strategy for ISS Deorbit Vehicle," SpaceNews, December 7, 2023, https://spacenews.com/nasa-revises-contract-strategy-for-iss-deorbit-vehicle/.

244   Platt, Kevin. "International Space Station Should Become a Museum 500 Miles above Earth," *Times of London*, June 7, 2022, https://www.thetimes.co.uk/article/international-space-station-should-become-museum-500-miles-above-earth-76xqk93hp.

245   Autry, Greg, and Mark Whittington. "Don't Trash the International Space Station," *Houston Chronicle*, December 8, 2023, https://www.houstonchronicle.com/opinion/outlook/article/international-space-station-preserve-18540760.php.

246   "Department of Defense and Full-Year Continuing Appropriations Act, 2011," US Public Law 112–10, sec. 1340, https://www.congress.gov/112/plaws/publ10/PLAW-112publ10.htm.

247   Dobrijevic, Daisy, and Andrew Jones. "China's Space Station, Tiangong: A Complete Guide," Space.com, August 15, 2023, https://www.space.com/tiangong-space-station.

248   Song, Wanyuan, and Jana Tauschinski. "China Space Station: What Is the Tiangong?," BBC, July 26, 2022, https://www.bbc.com/news/world-asia-china-61511546.

249   Jones, Andrew. "ESA Is No Longer Planning to Send Astronauts to China's Tiangong Space Station," SpaceNews, January 25, 2023, https://spacenews.com/esa-is-no-longer-planning-to-send-astronauts-to-chinas-tiangong-space-station/.

250   Jones, Andrew. "China Looks to Build Space Partnerships with Gulf Nations," SpaceNews, December 30, 2022, https://spacenews.com/china-looks-to-build-space-partnerships-with-gulf-nations/.

251   Bhandari, Konark. "Are We There Yet? The Artemis Accords, India, and the Way Forward," Carnegie India, March 28, 2023, https://carnegieindia.org/2023/03/28/are-we-there-yet-artemis-accords-india-and-way-forward-pub-89375.

252 Connell, Dylan, and Kate Halloran. "A Lunar Orbit That's Just Right for the International Gateway," NASA, May 16, 2022. https://www.nasa.gov/missions/artemis/lunar-near-rectilinear-halo-orbit-gateway/.

253 "The Vision for Space Exploration," NASA, February 2004, https://www.nasa.gov/wp-content/uploads/2023/01/55583main_vision_space_exploration2.pdf.

254 Connolly, John F. "Constellation Program Overview," NASA, October 2006, (via Internet Archive), https://web.archive.org/web/20070710060512/http://www.nasa.gov/pdf/163092main_constellation_program_overview.pdf.

255 Amos, Jonathan. "Obama Cancels Moon Return Project," BBC News, February 1, 2010, http://news.bbc.co.uk/1/hi/sci/tech/8489097.stm.

256 Oberg, James. "Soyuz-TMA—Improvements to the Russian Spacecraft," via SpaceNews, October 2002, http://www.jamesoberg.com/102002soyuztma_tec.html.

257 Mosher, Dave, and Skye Gould. "NASA Is Paying Russia More Than $70 Million to Bring an Astronaut Home in This Spaceship Tonight," *Business Insider*, September 6, 2016, https://www.businessinsider.com/space-travel-per-seat-cost-soyuz-2016-9.

258 Kramer, Miriam. "Russia's Deputy Prime Minister on Twitter: US Can Use Trampolines to Reach Space," Space.com, May 1, 2014, https://www.space.com/25718-russian-official-us-trampolines-space.html.

259 Duffy, Kate. "Elon Musk Points to Recent SpaceX Launch to Mock Russia's Suggestion the US Might Have to Fly into Space on 'Broomsticks' after Rocket Sales Stop," *Business Insider*, March 4, 2022, https://www.businessinsider.com/elon-musk-mocks-russia-space-chief-broomsticks-suggestion-spacex-launch-2022-3.

260 Rogin, Gilbert. "He's Not a Bird, He's Not a Plane," *Sports Illustrated*, February 5, 1968, https://vault.si.com/vault/1968/02/05/hes-not-a-bird-hes-not-a-plane.

261 Loumena, Dan. "Eddie Braun Does What Evel Knievel Could
     Not: Make Successful Jump over Snake River Canyon," *Los
     Angeles Times*, September 16, 2016, http://www.latimes.com/
     sports/sportsnow/la-sp-snake-river-canyon-jump-20160916-
     snap-story.html.

262 Regis, Ed. *Great Mambo Chicken and the Transhuman Condi-
     tion: Science Slightly over the Edge* (Basic Books, 1991).

263 Shapiro, T. Rees. "Rocket Scientist Robert C. Truax, Who
     Built Ship for Evel Knieval, Dies at 93," *Washington Post*, Sep-
     tember 29, 2010, https://www.washingtonpost.com/wp-dyn/
     content/article/2010/09/28/AR2010092805243.html.

264 Harrigan, Stephen. "Mr. Hannah's Rocket," *Texas Monthly*,
     November 1982, https://www.texasmonthly.com/news-poli-
     tics/mr-hannahs-rocket/.

265 Pappalardo, Joe. "Digging Up Regolith: Why Mining the
     Moon Seems More Possible Than Ever," *Popular Mechanics*,
     April 27, 2020, https://www.popularmechanics.com/space/
     moon-mars/a32253706/history-moon-mining/.

266 Brandt-Erichsen, David. "Brief History of the L5 Society," *Ad
     Astra*, November–December 1994.

267 Richman, Tom. "The Wrong Stuff," *Inc.*, July 1, 1982.

268 Harrigan, Stephen. "Mr. Hannah's Rocket," *Texas Monthly*,
     November 1982, https://www.texasmonthly.com/news-poli-
     tics/mr-hannahs-rocket/.

269 Hudson, Gary C., "GCH Companies & Projects," unpub-
     lished PDF, August 13, 2010, https://forum.nasaspace-
     flight.com/index.php?action=dlattach;topic=47798.0;at-
     tach=1554332;sess=0.

270 Peppard, Alan. "Reach for the Stars," *Dallas Morning News*,
     December 18, 2014, http://res.dallasnews.com/interactives/
     oilkings/part3/.

271 Butrica, Andrew J. "The Commercial Launch Industry, Reus-
     able Space Vehicles, and Technological Change," *Business and
     Economic History* 27, no. 1 (1998): 212–221, http://www.jstor.
     org/stable/23703084.

272 Hudson, Gary C. "GCH Companies & Projects," unpublished PDF, August 13, 2010, https://forum.nasaspaceflight.com/index.php?action=dlattach;topic=47798.0;attach=1554332;-sess=0.

273 "Conestoga 1620," Gunter's Space Page, accessed December 22, 2023, https://space.skyrocket.de/doc_lau_det/conesto-ga-1620.htm; Butrica, Andrew J. "The Commercial Launch Industry, Reusable Space Vehicles, and Technological Change," *Business and Economic History* 27, no. 1 (1998): 212–221, http://www.jstor.org/stable/23703084.

274 Schefter, J. "How They Build High-Tech Rockets on the Cheap," *Popular Science*, May 1984, https://archive.org/stream/popular_science_1984-05_may/popular_science_1984-05_may_djvu.txt.

275 "SpaceDev Acquires Hybrid Rocket Technology," *Space Daily*, August 14, 1998, https://www.spacedaily.com/news/spacedev-98e.html.

276 Coauthor Greg Autry's conversations with Rotary veterans Brian Binnie and Jeff Greason; "Rotary Rocket Appoints Barclays Capital," *Terra Daily*, January 21, 1998, https://www.terradaily.com/news/rlv-98b.html.

277 Manly, Scott. "Roton the Rotary Rocket," YouTube, April 2, 2019, https://youtu.be/OIuGfXp-Ok8.

278 Autry, Greg. "Exploring New Space: Governmental Roles in the Emergence of New Communities of High-Technology Organizations," (University of California, Irvine, 2013).

279 Cohn, Stanley. "What's Going Up in Zaire? OTRAG's Rocket Base in Shaba," *Munger Africana Library Notes*, April 1979, https://authors.library.caltech.edu/25694/1/MALN_49.pdf.

280 Wall, Kim et. al. "Naked in an Island Idyll: Eccentric Couple Recall a Life of Rockets and Dictators," *Guardian*, June 13, 2015, https://www.theguardian.com/travel/2015/jun/13/naked-island-idyll-eccentric-couple-recall-life-rockets-dicta-tors.

281 Chan, Sharon P. "The Birth and Demise of an Idea: Teledesic's 'Internet in the Sky,'" *Seattle Times*, Octo-

ber 7, 2002, https://archive.seattletimes.com/archive/?-date=20021007&slug=teledesic070.

282 Coauthor Greg Autry's conversations with Elon Musk.

283 Beal Aerospace Press Release, "Beal Aerospace Fires Largest Liquid Rocket Engine in 30 Years," SpaceRef, March 4, 2000, https://spaceref.com/press-release/beal-aerospace-fires-larg-est-liquid-rocket-engine-in-30-years/.

284 Pappalardo, J. "Love and Rockets," *Dallas Observer*, March 1, 2001, https://www.dallasobserver.com/news/love-and-rock-ets-6392592.

285 Pappalardo, J. *Spaceport Earth: The Reinvention of Spaceflight* (New York: Abrams, 2019); Beal, Andrew. Press Release Beal Aerospace, December 2001, https://www.spaceprojects.com/Beal/.

286 "Payload Specialist Bio: Charles D. Walker," NASA, February 1999, https://www.nasa.gov/wp-content/up-loads/2016/01/c-walker.pdf; Dubbs, Chris, and Emeline Paat-Dahlstrom. *Realizing Tomorrow: The Path to Private Spaceflight* (Lincoln: University of Nebraska Press, 2011).

287 "Payload Specialist Bio: Jake Garn," NASA, May 1985, https://www.nasa.gov/wp-content/uploads/2016/01/garn-j.pdf.

288 "Payload Specialist Bio: Bill Nelson," NASA , July 2008, https://www.nasa.gov/wp-content/uploads/2016/01/nel-son-b.pdf.

289 "Bill Nelson," NASA, https://www.nasa.gov/people/nasa-ad-ministrator-bill-nelson/.

290 "Payload Specialist Bio: Christa Corrigan McAuliffe," NASA, April 2007, https://www.nasa.gov/wp-content/up-loads/2016/01/mcauliffe.pdf.

291 Nadler, Gerald. "Soviets Launch Japanese reporter," UPI, De-cember 2, 1990, https://www.upi.com/Archives/1990/12/02/Soviets-launch-Japanese-reporter/9130660114000/.

292 Greg Autry in conversation with Helen Sharman at Imperial College London, December 16, 2023.

293 Dubbs, Chris, and Emeline Paat-Dahlstrom. *Realizing Tomorrow: The Path to Private Spaceflight* (Lincoln: University of Nebraska Press, 2011).

294 Wall, Mike. "First Space Tourist," Space.com, April 27, 2011, https://www.space.com/11492-space-tourism-pioneer-dennis-tito.html.

295 Greg Autry, personal conversations with Dennis Tito.

296 Weil, Elizabeth. "American Megamillionare Gets Russki Space Heap!," *New York Times*, July 2, 2000, https://www.nytimes.com/2000/07/23/magazine/american-megamillionaire-gets-russki-space-heap.html.

297 "About MirCorp 1999–2003," accessed December 24, 2023, http://mircorp.org/timeline.html; Greg Autry, personal conversations with Rick Tumlinson and Jeff Manber at various times; Messier, Doug. "Orphans of Anderson: Film Examines the Fall of Mir and a Tech Mogul," *Parabolic Arc*, March 16, 2009, https://web.archive.org/web/20100521065535/https://parabolicarc.com/2009/03/16/orphans-anderson-film-examines-fall-mir-tech-mogul/.

298 Wall, Mike. "First Space Tourist: How a U.S. Millionaire Bought a Ticket to Orbit," Space.com, April 27, 2011, https://www.space.com/11492-space-tourism-pioneer-dennis-tito.html.

299 David, Leonard. "NASA Chief Remains Miffed over Tito Launch," Space.Com, April 28, 2001, (via Internet Archive), https://web.archive.org/web/20090523162336/http://www.space.com/missionlaunches/missions/tito_pm_010428.html.

300 Mayeda, Julie. "The Forgotten Frontier/Whatever Happened to the United States' Space Program? There Seems to Be a Roadblock, and Surprisingly Enough, Its Name Is NASA," SFGate, January 18, 2004, https://www.sfgate.com/books/article/the-forgotten-frontier-whatever-happened-to-the-2829902.php.

301 "Who Needs NASA?," *Wired*, Jan 1, 2000, https://www.wired.com/2000/01/schmoes/.

302 Boyle, Alan. "SpaceShipOne Wins $10 Million X Prize," NBC News, October 3, 2004, https://www.nbcnews.com/id/wbna6167761.

303 Lemonick, Michael D. "ET, Call Us—Just Not Collect," *TIME*, April 28, 2011, https://content.time.com/time/health/article/0,8599,2067855,00.html.

304 Observation of coauthor Greg Autry at the inaugural SpaceShipOne spaceflight in June of 2004.

305 Observation of coauthor Greg Autry over many years at the Mojave Air and Space Port.

306 Observation of coauthor Greg Autry on the flightline at Mojave Air and Space Port in October of 2004.

307 Pearlman, Robert. "Soprano Sarah Brightman Reveals Mission Patch for Space Station Flight," Space.Com March 10, 2015, https://www.space.com/28781-sarah-brightman-space-mission-patch.html.

308 Boyle, Alan. "Spaceship Guru Roasts His Rivals," NBC News, May 4, 2006, https://www.nbcnews.com/id/wbna12634377.

309 Autry, Greg. *Exploring New Space: Governmental roles in the emergence of new communities of high-technology organizations* (PhD dissertation, University of California, Irvine, 2013).

310 Observation of coauthor Greg Autry in conversation with and listening to Elon Musk, Jeff Bezos, and Sir Richard Branson on various occasions.

311 White, F. *The Overview Effect: Space Exploration and Human Evolution* (Boston, MA: Houghton Mifflin,1987).

312 Sheetz, Michael. "William Shatner Emotionally Describes Spaceflight to Jeff Bezos: 'The Most Profound Experience,'" CNBC, October 14, 2021, https://www.cnbc.com/2021/10/13/william-shatner-speech-to-jeff-bezos-after-blue-origin-launch.html.

313 Hahn, Jason. "Billionaire Richard Branson Says Completing Lifelong Goal of Visiting Space Felt Like 'a Dream,'" *People*, July 14, 2021, https://people.com/human-interest/richard-branson-interview-virgin-galactic-unity-22-space.

225

314 Kranz, Gene. *Failure Is Not an Option* (Berkley Publishing, 2000).

315 Flatow, Ira, Teri Hamlin, and Mike Canga. "Early Space Shuttle Flights Riskier Than Estimated," *Talk of the Nation*, March 4, 2011, https://www.npr.org/2011/03/04/134265291/early-space-shuttle-flights-riskier-than-estimated.

316 Hedda, Benjamin. "How Many World Records Has Richard Branson Set," Screen Rant, December 13, 2022, https://screenrant.com/richard-branson-world-records-set-how-many/.

317 Isaacson, Walter. *Elon Musk* (OBJECTIVA, 2023).

318 Berger, Eric. *Liftoff: Elon Musk and the Desperate Early Days That Launched SpaceX* (New York: HarperCollins, 2021).

319 Zapata, Edgar. "An Assessment of Cost Improvements in the NASA COTS/CRS Program and Implications for Future NASA Missions," AIAA, accessed December 30, 2023, https://ntrs.nasa.gov/api/citations/20170008895/downloads/20170008895.pdf.

320 SpaceX.com, accessed December 27, 2023, https://www.spacex.com/.

321 MacDonald, Cheyenne. "SpaceX Dominated Private Spaceflight in 2023, but Its Competitors (Mostly) Aren't Quitting," Engadget, December 21, 2023, https://www.engadget.com/spacex-dominated-private-spaceflight-in-2023-but-its-competitors-mostly-arent-quitting-153050005.html.

322 "Shenzhou Flight History" and "Crew Dragon Flight History," Gunter's Space Page, accessed December 27, 2023, https://space.skyrocket.de/doc_sat/shenzhou_hist.htm and https://space.skyrocket.de/doc_sat/dragon.htm.

323 Xin, Ling. "China Space Authorities Name Elon Musk's SpaceX an 'Unprecedented Challenge,'" *South China Morning Post*, December 6, 2023, https://www.scmp.com/news/china/science/article/3244086/china-space-authorities-name-elon-musks-spacex-unprecedented-challenge.

324 Boyle, Alan. "Gradatim Ferociter! Jeff Bezos Explains Blue Origin's Motto, Logo…and the Boots," Geek Wire, October

24, 2016, https://www.geekwire.com/2016/jeff-bezos-blue-origin-motto-logo-boots/.

325   Wall, Mike. "Artemis 1 Moon Rocket, NASA's Most Powerful Ever, Aced Its Debut Launch, Says Agency," Space.com, December 1, 2022, https://www.space.com/artemis-1-sls-moon-rocket-aced-debut-launch.

326   Davenport, Christian. "CEO of Jeff Bezos's Blue Origin Rocket Company Resigns," September 25, 2023, https://www.washingtonpost.com/technology/2023/09/25/blue-origin-space-ceo-resigns/.

327   Reported to coauthor Greg Autry by multiple sources.

328   Howell, Elizabeth. "Blue Origin Will Launch an 18-Year-Old as Its Final Passenger on 1st Crewed Flight," Space.com, July 15, 2021, https://www.space.com/blue-origin-18-year-old-passenger-identity-revealed.

329   Pasztor, Andy. "Jeff Bezos's Blue Origin Succeeds in Landing Spent Rocket Back on Earth," *Wall Street Journal*, November 24, 2015, https://www.wsj.com/articles/blue-origin-succeeds-in-vertically-landing-spent-rocket-back-at-texas-launch-site-1448372666.

330   Gannon, Megan. "20 Years Ago: Novel DC-X Reusable Rocket Launched into History," Space.com, August 16, 2013, https://www.space.com/22391-reusable-rocket-nasa-dc-x-anniversary.html.

331   "Branson's Virgin Galactic Reaches Edge of Space," BBC December 13, 2018, https://www.bbc.com/news/business-46550862.

332   Chen, Stephen. "China Declares Price War on SpaceX Reusable Rockets, with Economy Driving New Aerospace Programme," *South China Morning Post*, April 6, 2023, https://www.scmp.com/news/china/science/article/3216170/china-declares-price-war-spacex-reusable-rockets-economy-driving-new-aerospace-programme.

333   Observation of Greg Autry during a visit to ULA HQ in 2007.

334 Observation of Greg Autry in discussions with Andy Lambert.

335 Morring, Frank Jr. "China Great Wall Confounded by SpaceX Prices," *Aviation Week*, April 15, 2011, https://aviationweek.com/china-great-wall-confounded-spacex-prices.

336 Davenport, Christian. "Elon Musk's SpaceX Settles Lawsuit against Air Force," January 23, 2015, https://www.washingtonpost.com/business/economy/elon-musks-spacex-to-drop-lawsuit-against-air-force/2015/01/23/c5e8ff80-a34c-11e4-9f89-561284a573f8_story.html; Sheetz, Michael. "Just Revealed SpaceX Lawsuit Alleges Air Force 'Wrongly Awarded' Billions to Rocket Competitors," CNBC, May 22, 2019, https://www.cnbc.com/2019/05/22/spacex-lawsuit-challenges-air-force-rocket-awards-to-competitors-including-jeff-bezos-blue-origin.html.

337 Wright, Robert. "SpaceX Mocks Rival in Tetchy Congressional Hearing," *Financial Times*, Mach 17, 2015, https://www.ft.com/content/53043498-ccec-11e4-b5a5-00144feab7de.

338 "Rocket Lab Unveils Plans for New 8-Ton Class Reusable Rocket for Mega-Constellation Deployment," Business Wire, March 1, 2021, https://www.businesswire.com/news/home/20210301005406/en/Rocket-Lab-Unveils-Plans-for-New-8-Ton-Class-Reusable-Rocket-for-Mega-Constellation-Deployment.

339 Berger, Eric. "After a Remarkable Resurrection, Firefly May Reach Space in 2019," Ars Technica, February 11, 2019, https://arstechnica.com/science/2019/02/firefly-returns-from-the-dead-with-a-larger-rocket-and-lunar-aspirations.

340 Foust, Jeff. "AE Industrial Partners to Acquire Stake in Firefly from Noosphere," SpaceNews, February 24, 2022, https://spacenews.com/ae-industrial-partners-to-acquire-stake-in-firefly-from-noosphere.

341 Wall, Mike. "New Record! Firefly Aerospace Launches Space Force Mission 27 Hours after Receiving Order," Space.com, September 15, 2023, https://www.space.com/firefly-aerospace-rapid-launch-space-force-success.

342 Kuthunur, Sharmila. "Virgin Orbit Files for Bankruptcy after Funding Efforts Fail," Space.com, April 4, 2023, https://www.space.com/virgin-orbit-files-for-bankruptcy.

343 Observations by coauthor Greg Autry on several occasions at Virgin Orbit and Rocket Lab in Long Beach, California.

344 Jones, Andrew. "Who Is Relativity Space and What Do They Do?," Space.com, April 25, 2023, https://www.space.com/relativity-space.

345 Bhattacharya, Bidushi, Greg Autry, and Veronica Perry. "Relativity Space: Rocketing into the Future of Manufacturing," Lloyd Greif Center Case Collection via HBSP, July 15, 2020; Autry, Greg, and Tim Ellis. "Racing for Place in the New Space Race: Customers Seek Launch Options," *Forbes*, November 15, 2023, https://www.forbes.com/sites/gregautry/2023/11/15/racing-for-place-in-the-new-space-race-customers-seek-launch-options.

346 "Spaceports by State," FAA, accessed December 27, 2023, https://www.faa.gov/space/spaceports_by_state.

347 Feltman, Damon et al. "An Assessment of the Commercial Spaceport Ecosystem through the Lens of Cape Canaveral Space Force Station," *New Space* 11, no. 4 (December 2023).

348 de Selding, Peter B. "China Eyes Purchase of Sea Launch Assets," SpaceNews, July 17, 2015, https://spacenews.com/china-eyes-purchase-of-sea-launch-assets/.

349 Jones, Andrew. "China Launches 14 Satellites with Solid Rocket from Mobile Sea Platform," SpaceNews, December 9, 2022, https://spacenews.com/china-launches-14-satellites-with-new-solid-rocket-from-mobile-sea-platform/.

350 Xin, Ling. "Chinese Firm Launches Satellite from Mobile Sea Platform, Testing Potential Tech for National Space Programme," *South China Morning Post*, September 6, 2023, https://www.scmp.com/news/china/science/article/3233570/chinese-firm-launches-satellite-mobile-sea-platform-testing-potential-tech-national-space-programmes.

351 Abbany, Zulfikar. "Will Offshore Launches Solve the Spaceport Bottleneck?," DW, December 1, 2023, https://www.

dw.com/en/will-offshore-launches-solve-the-spaceport-bot-tleneck/a-67573892.

352 Bates, Jason. "EELV Launches Dished Evenly to Boeing and Lockheed Martin," Space.com, April 11, 2005, https://www.space.com/945-eelv-launches-dished-evenly-boeing-lock-heed-martin.html.

353 "Two Former Boeing Managers Charged in Plot to Steal Trade Secrets from Lockheed Martin," US Department of Justice, June 25, 2003, https://www.justice.gov/archive/crimi-nal/cybercrime/press-releases/2003/branchCharge.htm.

354 Autry, Greg. "A Dangerous Partnership with Russia," *Washington Times*, February 7, 2016, https://www.washington-times.com/news/2016/feb/7/greg-autry-a-dangerous-part-nership-with-russia/.

355 Berger, Eric. "Where Are My Engines, Jeff?—Blue Origin's Powerful BE-4 Engine Is More Than Four Years Late—Here's Why," Ars Technica, August 5, 2021, https://arstechnica.com/science/2021/08/blue-origins-powerful-be-4-engine-is-more-than-four-years-late-heres-why/.

356 "Vulcan," ULA, accessed December 28, 2023, https://www.ulalaunch.com/rockets/vulcan-centaur.

357 "Capabilities & Services," SpaceX, accessed December 28, 2023, https://www.spacex.com/media/Capabilities&Services.pdf.

358 Coauthor Greg Autry in conversation with Tory Bruno; de Selding, Peter B. "ULA Touts Mid-Air Recovery as More Cost-Effective Than SpaceX's Reusability Plan," SpaceNews, September 30, 2015, https://spacenews.com/ula-touts-mid-air-recovery-as-more-cost-effective-than-spacexs-reusabili-ty-plan/.

359 Maidenberg, Micah. "Jeff Bezos' Rocket Startup and Cer-berus Compete to Buy SpaceX Rival," *Wall Street Journal*, December 21, 2023, https://www.wsj.com/business/billion-aires-compete-to-own-spacexs-rocket-rival-d5ab16d4.

360 Foust, Jeff. "Strong Interest for SpaceX Smallsat Rideshare Launch Services," SpaceNews, February 9, 2021, https://spa-

cenews.com/spacex-sees-strong-demand-for-smallsat-ride-share-launch-services/.

361 Lea, Robert. "Artemis 1 Cubesats: The 10 Tiny Satellites Hitching a NASA Ride to the Moon," Space.com, August 25, 2022, https://www.space.com/nasa-artemis-1-moon-mission-cubesats.

362 Berger, Eric. "SpaceX Engineer Says NASA Should Plan for Starship's 'Significant' Capability," Ars Technica, May 2, 2022, https://arstechnica.com/science/2022/05/spacex-engineer-says-nasa-should-plan-for-starships-significant-capability/.

363 Berger, Eric. "China's State Rocket Company Unveils Rendering of a Starship Look-Alike," Ars Technica, April 26, 2021, https://arstechnica.com/science/2021/04/chinas-state-rocket-company-unveils-rendering-of-a-starship-look-alike/.

364 Sun Tzu, *The Art of War*, trans. John Minford (New York: Penguin Books, 2006).

365 "Treaty on Principles Governing the Activities of States in the Exploration and Use of Outer Space, including the Moon and Other Celestial Bodies," UN Office for Outer Space Affairs, accessed December 28, 2023, https://www.unoosa.org/oosa/en/ourwork/spacelaw/treaties/outerspacetreaty.html.

366 Chang, Kenneth. "China Lucks Out Again as Out-of-Control Rocket Booster Falls in the Pacific," *New York Times*, November 5, 2022, https://www.nytimes.com/2022/11/04/science/china-rocket-debris.html.

367 Zak, Anatoly. "Disaster at Xichang," *Smithsonian Magazine*, February 2013, https://www.smithsonianmag.com/air-space-magazine/disaster-at-xichang-2873673/.

368 "China: Possible Missile Technology Transfers under U.S. Satellite Export Policy—Actions and Chronology," *EveryCRSReport.com*, August 13, 1998–October 6, 2023, https://www.everycrsreport.com/reports/98-485.html.

369 "Annual Number of Objects Launched into Space, UNOSSA," *Our World in Data*, accessed December 29, 2023, https://

ourworldindata.org/grapher/yearly-number-of-objects-launched-into-outer-space.

370 Zinger, Kurtis J. "An Overreaction That Destroyed an Industry: The Past, Present, and Future of U.S. Satellite Export Controls," (JD diss., October 26, 2014), http://lawreview.colorado.edu/wp-content/uploads/2015/07/13.-86.1-Zinger_Final.pdf.

371 Berger, Eric. "Citing Slow Starship Reviews, SpaceX Urges FAA to Double Licensing Staff," Ars Technica, October 17, 2023, https://arstechnica.com/space/2023/10/citing-slow-starship-reviews-spacex-urges-faa-to-double-licensing-staff/.

372 Observation of Greg Autry in many interactions with industry and FAA/AST.

373 Foust, Jeff. "Varda Partners with Australian Range for Capsule Landings," SpaceNews, October 23, 2023, https://spacenews.com/varda-partners-with-australian-range-for-capsule-landings/.

374 Clark, Stephen. "Varda Looks to Australia after Delays in Obtaining US Reentry Approval," Ars Technica, October 19, 2023, accessed December 29, 2023, https://arstechnica.com/space/2023/10/varda–looks–to–australia–after–delays–in–obtaining–us–reentry–approval/.

375 Foust, Jeff. "Varda Gets Reentry License for Space Manufacturing Capsule," SpaceNews, February 14, 2024, accessed February 18, 2023, https://spacenews.com/varda-gets-reentry-license-for-space-manufacturing-capsule.

376 Pisani, Joseph. "SpaceX Project's FAA Review Delayed after Receiving 18,000 Comments," *Wall Street Journal*, December 29, 2021, https://www.wsj.com/articles/spacex-projects-faa-review-delayed-after-receiving-18-000-comments-11640811325.

377 Aragon, Rose-Ann. "Starship Boca Chica Site Is Also Rich with History and Biodiversity," Click2Houston, December 1, 2020, https://www.click2houston.com/news/local/2020/12/02/starship-boca-chica-site-is-also-rich-with-history-and-biodiversity/.

378 "Starships and Stripes Forever: An Examination of FAA's Role in the Future of Spaceflight," US Department of Transportation, June 16, 2021, https://www.transportation.gov/testimony/starships-and-stripes-forever-examination-faas-role-future-spaceflight.

379 "Mission," Office of Space Commerce, accessed December 29, 2023, https://www.space.commerce.gov/about/mission/.

380 Hao, Nicole. "Beijing Capitalizes on Elon Musk Satellite Incident for Propaganda Purposes," *Epoch Times*, December 29, 2021, https://www.theepochtimes.com/china/china-style-propaganda-urges-us-to-act-responsibly-in-space-to-show-its-muscles-4182093.

381 Lyons, Kim. "Ireland's Status as Tax Haven for Tech Firms Like Google, Facebook, and Apple Is Ending," *The Verge*, October 7, 2021, https://www.theverge.com/2021/10/7/22715229/ireland-status-tax-haven-google-facebook-apple.

382 Trump, Donald J. "Space Policy Directive-3, National Space Traffic Management Policy," June 18, 2018, https://trumpwhitehouse.archives.gov/presidential-actions/space-policy-directive-3-national-space-traffic-management-policy/.

383 Foust, Jeff. "GAO Report Warns Artemis 3 Landing May Be Delayed to 2027," SpaceNews, December 1, 2023, https://spacenews.com/gao-report-warns-artemis-3-landing-may-be-delayed-to-2027.

384 O'Shea, Claire A. "NASA Selects Blue Origin as Second Artemis Lunar Lander Provider," NASA, May 19, 2023, https://www.nasa.gov/news-release/nasa-selects-blue-origin-as-second-artemis-lunar-lander-provider/.

385 "Artemis Accords," US Department of State, accessed December 29, 2023, https://www.state.gov/artemis-accords/.

386 "The Artemis Accords," NASA, accessed December 29, 2023, https://www.nasa.gov/wp-content/uploads/2022/11/Artemis-Accords-signed-13Oct2020.pdf.

387 Autry, Greg. "Pennywise, Future Foolish: Congress Moves to Cut NASA Science Budget," *Forbes*, July 27, 2023, https://

www.forbes.com/sites/gregautry/2023/07/27/pennywise-fu-ture-foolish-congress-moves-to-cut-nasa-science-budget.

388 "F-35 Joint Strike Force Fighter," GAO, July 13, 2021, https://www.gao.gov/assets/gao-21-105282-highlights.pdf.

389 "Medicare Funds Totaling $60 Billion Improperly Paid, Report Finds," ABC News, July 23, 2015, https://abcnews.go.com/Politics/medicare-funds-totaling-60-billion-improp-erly-paid-report/story?id=32604330.

390 Tacitus. *Annals* 15:50, a popular rendering of: "nisi impunita-tis cupido retinuisset, magnis semper conatibus adversa," lit-erally: "but desire of escape, foe to all great enterprises, held him back." This was said of Subrius Flavus's passing thought of assassinating Nero while the emperor sang on stage.

391 "The Mineral Supply Chain and the New Space Race," House Committee on Natural Resources, Oversight and Investigations Subcommittee, December 12, 2023, https://naturalresources.house.gov/calendar/eventsingle.aspx?Even-tID=415257.

ABOUT THE AUTHORS

Dr. Greg Autry is Director of Space Leadership, Policy, and Business in the Thunderbird School of Global Management and a professor at Arizona State University. He holds appointments as an affiliate professor at ASU's Interplanetary Initiative and as a visiting professor at Imperial College London.

Dr. Autry served on the NASA agency review team and as White House liaison at NASA. He was nominated by President Trump to serve as NASA's chief financial officer and also served on the Commercial Space Transportation Advisory Committee (COMSTAC) at the FAA. He is the vice president of the National Space Society.

Dr. Autry's writings are frequently published in *Foreign Policy*, *Forbes*, and *SpaceNews*. He appears regularly on major media outlets and is widely quoted on space-related topics. He is a serial technology entrepreneur and the author of *A New Entrepreneurial Dynamic* (FlatWorld, 2022). He serves on the editorial review boards of the *New Space Journal* and the *Journal of Space Safety Engineering*. Dr. Autry holds an MBA and PhD from the University of California, Irvine.

Peter Navarro is one of only three senior White House officials with President Trump from the 2016 presidential campaign to the end of term. Navarro served as manufacturing czar and was a principal architect of Trump's tariff, trade, and "tough on China" policies.

Navarro is a noted China scholar, acclaimed public speaker, and award-winning professor emeritus at the University of California, Irvine. His books include the bestselling *In Trump Time*, *Taking Back Trump's America*, and *The Coming China Wars*.

Navarro holds a PhD in economics and master's in public administration from Harvard University. He has appeared frequently on major media outlets, regularly guest-hosts Steve Bannon's *War Room*, and appears often on Newsmax and Real America's Voice.

Made in the USA
Middletown, DE
23 June 2024

56174396R00146